MALIBU

THE MAN'S
GOURMET
SEX BOOK

BY PEGGY &
EVAN BURKE

"But to see her
was to love her,
Love but her,
and love forever."

-Robert Burns,
Ae Fond Kiss

INTRODUCTION

The price of this book may be the best investment of your lifetime! It is an investment that will pay dividends for many years to come; for, unlike other books that are made to be read and then cast aside, *The Man's Gourmet Sex Book* is a book that will prove more valuable each time it is put to use.

The book is about love and sex, sex and love, but it is not just another sex manual; it is, instead, a book designed to open your eyes to, and increase your enjoyment of, each and every possibility for pleasure that exists in any relationship between a man and a woman.

A day-to-day guide to assist in the development of your skills as a lover, *The Gourmet Sex Book* offers hundreds of suggestions on sexual positions and technique. But that is not all it offers.

As you begin to put *The Gourmet Sex Book* to use, you will find many individual entries which are designed to help you overcome any inhibitions either of you may have, others that simply encourage the intimate contact that must be established prior to any sexual act, and still others that will convey to your mate the affection you feel.

The latter group is extremely important, for a very simple reason which you should keep in mind: When a man thinks of love, he thinks of sex; when a woman thinks of sex, she thinks of love . . .

Thus, even though love, in the deepest meaning of the word, may not be a part of the relationship you have established, or wish to establish, with the woman of the moment, affection remains a necessary ingredient if the relationship is to be mutually enjoyable. She will welcome these small displays of affection and repay them by becoming a better partner in physical love.

You will find it necessary to exercise your own judgment as you put to use many of the suggestions that are sexual in nature, for only you can judge in advance how the individual female will react to your overtures; any book that suggests otherwise is misleading. You will discover, however, that *The Gourmet Sex Book* does suggest many ways in which her attitudes may be explored, and many techniques that will make her more eager to participate in the sexual acts she may have previously avoided.

It is for this reason that many of the individual entries do not suggest the

manner in which the ultimate act should be completed. The daily entries of this type may suggest an oral technique, a unique type of foreplay, or the exploration of one of her erogenous zones. In this way your attention is drawn to the single aspect of sexuality suggested for that day; and though you will, in many cases, want to combine it with techniques you know she finds exciting, you will have added another weapon to your sexual arsenal.

As the days and weeks pass and you show her how varied and exciting your lovemaking can be, you will certainly find that her own bedroom manner becomes more open and her sexual imagination more active. That is the time, if the relationship you share with her is one you want to last and grow, when you may wish to present her with a copy of *The Woman's Gourmet Sex Book,* the companion of this book. It will show her the full potential of her sexuality and, while helping her shed the last of her inhibitions, show her how she may make every night a better one for you.

As you begin to use *The Gourmet Sex Book,* you may find that a few of the suggestions do not appeal to you; or, you may decide, they are beyond the scope of your relationship and would not appeal to the woman in your life. Give these careful consideration before you reject them — being absolutely sure that you are giving equal weight to her wants and needs — and try to keep an open mind about them, as you may want to experiment with them later.

Should you decide to reject the suggestion for a certain date in the book, do your best to think of a new and stimulating technique to replace it. When you do this, you will have taken a giant step toward achieving creative sexuality, which is the ultimate purpose of this book, and you will find yourself adding your own refinements to the techniques suggested in the book.

The Gourmet Sex Book is arranged in the form of a perpetual calendar, so it can be used year after year. Put it to use by turning to today's date, reading the entry, and letting your mind dwell for a while on the act that is suggested there before attempting to make it a reality. Sensuality is, to a certain degree, a frame of mind, and this delay between the thought and the act will help to create that frame of mind — an attitude that is highly contagious and will bring her eagerly into your arms.

Happy loving!

January 1

Time to make those New Year's resolutions, and to do that you must first decide what needs to be changed. Try to take an objective look at your attitudes and behavior during the year gone by.

Was your lovemaking directed toward your mate's pleasure as much as your own? Did you really attempt to make each session of love an exciting new adventure? Did you search for new ways of pleasing her, and were you careful to treat her as an equal partner in the act of love?

How many new techniques and positions did you explore during the months gone by, and how many times did you withdraw abruptly after intercourse rather than give her the tender and continuing assurances of love she wants and needs?

Give yourself honest answers to these questions; find the areas that need improvement, and resolve to make those improvements during the year that begins today.

January 2

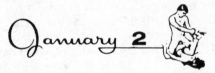

Leave work early today.

As soon as you are with her, take her in your arms and let her know you did this because you were so eager to be with her—and let your eagerness show as you kiss her and use your hands to stroke and caress her body, stripping away her clothes.

Not only will she be excited and flattered by the knowledge that you wanted so badly to be with her, but the unexpectedness of your arrival and the love-making at a time that breaks your regular pattern will cause the act to be especially pleasurable for both of you.

January 3

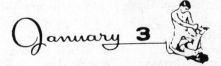

Take a careful look at your personal hygiene. A very careful look. Though it should go without saying, nothing turns a woman off faster than a foul body odor, bad breath, or a scratchy beard that tortures her tender skin; yet it is all too easy for a man—especially after his relationship with a woman has grown lengthy—to ignore some of the basics of cleanliness. Don't fall into this trap.

In addition to the basics of showering, shaving, and brushing that should be a regular pre-love routine, add to your toilet a wide array of colognes. Not only are they masculine and nearly essential to good grooming but most of the scents are carefully created to appeal to her erotic senses as well.

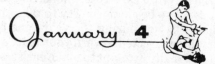

January 4

Do you always strip away all her clothing before making love?

Most men do, and the feel of naked flesh against naked flesh is wonderful to all concerned, but you can give her new sensations of delight by taking her almost fully clothed. Why not give her those sensations tonight?

After your kisses and caressing hands have so excited her that her writhing body tells you she is ready for sex, remove only her panties and use your weight to press her down against the sofa or bed. Free your penis for action, slip her skirt up under her buttocks, and, if possible, uncover her breasts so you can take her nipples into your mouth. Then take her with hard, pounding thrusts of your penis.

Lovemaking of this type, with its suggestion of desperate need on your part, and with her clothing in a state of disarray, gives a woman a feeling of being ravaged—and even the most domineering female will love you for doing that to her, lovingly, now and then!

January 5

Buy her a subscription to a feminist magazine—and see what the feminists can do for *you!*

You may be surprised to discover they can do a lot. Though major portions of each issue of these publications are devoted to social and political topics, they also stress equality in sexual relations. Article after article is dedicated to the idea that sex is a thing to be equally enjoyed, and the writers repeatedly attack the old taboos against oral and anal sex—when these acts are agreeable to the female partner, of course.

Nothing will cause her to shed any inhibitions she may have faster than an awareness that other women are participating in the entire realm of sexuality. So why not have the articles that will make her aware delivered to her front door on the first of each month?

January 6

Tonight show her what those hands of yours can do!

Immediately after you have finished making love, and while she still simmers with the afterglow of passion, take her in your arms and kiss her with open lips. As you let your tongue explore her mouth, slip one hand over the soft mound of her pubis. Move your fingers in a slow circle, then up and down, then once again in a circle, increasing the pressure until she begins to writhe.

Move your lips to her breasts and suck her nipples as you continue to massage her *mons,* and soon you will feel her clawing your back as she reaches orgasm after orgasm—even though she may have climaxed repeatedly during your previous lovemaking.

Many women experience their most intense orgasms when stroked in this manner and at this time; and there is an added advantage for you in that your own actions will soon have you hard and ready to resume where you left off.

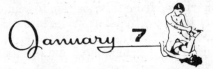

January 7

Cunnilingus is one of the most exciting acts a man can perform, and to do it expertly, you need complete control over the movements of your tongue. Here is an exercise that will help you gain that control. Try it today and practice it often.

Extend the tongue fully. Keeping it stiff, move it from side to side, touching each corner of your mouth. Repeat this action thirty times—and keep it in mind when you are with her.

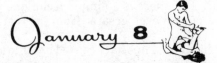

January 8

Most women are subject to anal stimulation, you know, and you can use this type of stimulation to greatly increase her enjoyment of sexual intercourse. So why not give her this dual pleasure tonight.

Use prolonged foreplay to make her unbearably eager for sexual relief, and then, with your legs together, draw her into a kneeling position over your erected penis. As you enter her, pull her down so that her naked breasts are against your chest, then grasp her buttocks and hold her with her groin touching yours.

Let your hands spread her buttocks as she begins to writhe, then press them together. Repeat this movement a few times, and then, holding her buttocks apart, touch the tip of one finger to her anus. Apply pressure slowly, letting the pumping of her hips force her anus around your finger, and soon she will be bucking back and forth, overcome by the thrill of this double penetration.

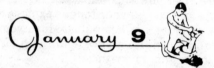

$\mathcal{J}$anuary 9

Are you sometimes at a loss as to the best way of letting her know you want to perform cunnilingus? The best way is to use no words at all. Try this method tonight.

Take her in your arms and begin kissing her; then, while she still wears her clothes, let your lips wander down to her breasts and from there to the soft rise of her stomach. Nuzzle her lovingly in the vee of her thighs, pressing your face against her pubis, and she will quickly get the message.

It is but a short step from this position to a kneeling one that allows you to cover her thighs with hot arousing kisses; and she will know exactly what you intend to do as you remove her panties and prove it by parting her thighs to let your tongue and lips play over her moist and quivering vulva.

$\mathcal{J}$anuary 10

Clitoral stimulation is the basis of most female orgasms, and in most cases friction against the clitoris is greater when the penis is inserted from the front. But there is a simple technique you can use to make that delicious friction even greater from the rear, so why not give it a try tonight?

When your hands and lips have coaxed her into a state of near-nudity and she is anxious to feel the thrust of your penis, have her lie on her side while you hold her from behind, her buttocks nestled against your groin and your penis probing high between her thighs.

As you insert your penis and begin moving it in and out, let your hands wander over her breasts, skillfully teasing her erected nipples, and slowly move one hand down to her stomach, then even lower. Fan your fingers out over the soft, hairy mound above her vagina, and apply a gentle but steady pressure.

As the strokes of your hardened penis grow faster and longer, use your fingers to move that delectably soft mound in slow, sensuous circles, which will keep her all-important clitoris in constant contact with your hard and thrusting penis; and be sure to let her feel the touch of your lips against her shoulders and neck, the fingers of your other hand adoringly stroking her breasts.

It will soon have her trembling with the most violent orgasms she has ever known—while she begs for more!

January 11

Tonight explore an erogenous zone that many men overlook—her eyes!

As you take her in your arms, touch your lips gently to one eye, then the other. Move your lips to cover the sides of her face with tender little kisses, and let her feel your tongue parting her lips to probe deep in her mouth, but let your kisses return time after time to her eyes. Let her feel the tip of your tongue touching her lashes and the outer corners of her closed eyes.

The sexual stirrings caused by your caresses on her eyes will be fairly mild compared to those she experiences when you let your lips and fingers play over her breasts or clitoris, but she will feel them all the same, and these tender kisses convey to her a feeling that you feel a real devotion toward her. Combined with the gentle stroking of your hands on her body, the pressure of your erection against her, these gentle kisses can be highly arousing—as you will soon discover.

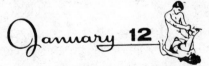

January 12

Fellatio can be an extremely exciting form of foreplay for both you and her. But when she fellates you to a climax, though she is most certainly aroused by the act, your release does little to satisfy her own needs.

Give her full satisfaction tonight—and then some!

Encourage her to take you into her mouth tonight, either by asking or by placing yourself above her as you use your lips and tongue on her vagina, and then verbally praise her skills so that she will continue until you have climaxed.

But don't stop now!

Even though, as many men would be at this point, you are inclined to lie back and relax, remember that the act of taking your penis into her mouth and fellating it has left her in dire need of sexual fulfillment.

Give her this fulfillment by immediately turning to place your face between her parted thighs and letting your tongue lap at her moistened vagina until the sudden straining tautness of her body tells you she has reached orgasm. That will be very soon, because her own oral performance had her ready. And you will find that *your* oral performance has brought you once again to a state of readiness—which will make you more than welcome as you settle yourself between her thighs.

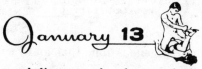

January 13

Take her skiing—and discover why the popularity of this sport is booming.

At this time of the year, in almost any part of the country, it is only a short drive to a ski slope. Artificial snow has made this possible, and beginners' slopes make it a sport for all.

You will find that this is a sport that encourages physical contact between any couple sharing the slopes, and the lodges at most resorts seem designed to encourage contact of a far more intimate nature. Romance is encouraged by drinks shared before a glowing fireplace, and the entire atmosphere is calculated to cause a feeling of closeness and relaxation.

Just be sure to pick a resort where rooms are available for the night. Then let your love take care of her longings.

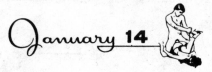

January 14

Given a choice between prolonged sexual intercourse and intercourse that is repeated time after time, which do you suppose most women would choose? The answer, in most cases, would be intercourse that is prolonged. That is because, once she has reached orgasm, the continuing friction against her clitoris, with no interval in which she remains untouched, can cause her to climax repeatedly.

Tonight you are going to give her that prolonged session of sexual intercourse.

As you begin making love to her, assume a position that will allow you to reach down with one hand and grasp the base of the shaft of your penis. A rear-entry position, with you standing or kneeling behind her, is probably the best for this purpose.

Let your penis glide in and out of her until you feel yourself nearing climax; and then, easing it out until only the tip remains within her, grasp the shaft tightly, so your fingers are pressing hard against the thick cord that runs the length of the underside. Grip it like this until you feel the urge to ejaculate pass—about five or six seconds, usually—and then resume where you left off.

You will find it quite easy to postpone your climax time after time in this manner—and while you are delaying your own release, she will be shaking with orgasms far too numerous to count.

But who keeps score?

Discover for yourself why blondes prefer *gentlemen*.

Take her out for dinner and dancing. As you help her with her coat, and as you help her in and out of the car, let her feel the most casual touch of your hands. At the dinner table, reach out to place your hand over hers; and as you dance, let your hands gradually move to more intimate spots—but not too intimate.

When at last you are alone and you take her in your arms to make love, you will find that she is far more relaxed and ready to respond than if you had been abrupt with your advances . . . and this is true in even the longest of relationships. It is true because those carefully planned but casual touches have renewed in her the feeling that it is right and proper for her to be in your arms.

Try to talk her out of her panties—and everything else she is wearing!

Sex talk is very exciting to most females, though many refuse to admit it, and you can use it to stimulate her to the same extent as you would with physical caresses.

Begin by flattering her breasts, legs, buttocks or any area of her body of which she is especially proud, and teasingly ask her to display it for you. Don't take no for an answer. Tell her how excited you are by the sight of her naked breasts—or whatever—and coax her into baring that part of her body. Then go to work on the next. Then the next. Express your pleasure as she strips away each garment, and describe in teasing, sexy detail what the sight of her naked flesh makes you want to do.

Shy as she may sometimes appear to be, it is highly likely that she will surprise you—after a little coaxing—by readily complying with your requests. Or she may respond by telling you to remove the garments yourself.

Which is a fair enough compromise.

January 17

Let anal foreplay precede anal intercourse.

Relaxation of the rectal muscles is the key to her enjoyment of anal intercourse, so try using seductive caresses of your lips and hands to put her in a mood that will make this act as pleasing to her as it is to you.

When first you take her into your arms to kiss her, let your hands gently massage her buttocks, spreading the pliable mounds, and after her panties are removed, continue to center your attentions on her rear.

As she begins to undulate against you, slowly part her buttocks and press one finger against her anus. Slip it slowly in, being careful to cause her no pain, and move it back and forth until you feel her hips begin to pump in arousal. Then, when she is fully agreeable to the fact of anal intercourse, you be the one who applies the lubricant to her body, and do it with motions which will increase her arousal.

You will find that your attentions have relaxed the muscles surrounding her anus, making your entry much easier, and she will be much more likely to enjoy your anal penetration.

January 18

Here is a position she will love!

Tonight, when you have used your hands, lips and tongue to fill her body with simmering desire, draw her into a standing embrace as you prepare to remove her panties. Slowly drop to your knees as you tug the garment down her legs, and as she steps out of them, press your lips breifly to her vulva, your hands grasping the back of her thighs.

As you slowly return to an erect position, letting your lips lead the way up her body, place one hand under her buttocks. Use that hand to steady her as you encourage her to lift one leg and wrap it around your body, and then place both hands under her buttocks.

As you lift her slightly and guide her over your erection, she will automatically wrap her arms around your neck; and she will sigh with pleasure as the weight of her own body causes her to settle over the full length of your hardened penis.

January 19

Do the dishes for her.

There is no easier way to show your affectioon for her than to take this simple chore off her hands now and then. Do it without even mentioning it to her, and the surprise will be even more meaningful.

Not only does this simple gesture show her how much you care, it also allows her to rest and save her energy for the reward she will want to give you later . . . in the bedroom.

January 20

Let her control the motions—and the pace—of sex.

As the two of you begin to make love, lie on your back, your legs together and extended, and draw her into a kneeling position that places her vagina directly over your erected penis.

Use your hands to guide her onto your erection, lifting your hips until your shaft is in her, then settle back and let her take it from there— at least for the present.

Let your hands caress her breasts, stomach, thighs and buttocks, as she begins to move herself over your penis, but keep your hips immobile, giving her complete control of the speed and depth of penetration.

Most women like to assume the dominant role now and then, and she will probably begin slowly at first, perhaps covering only the tip of your penis with her wetness, but soon her hips will begin to pump with reckless abandon, and yours will do the same.

That is when both of you lose control.

January 21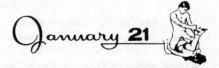

Try wearing a pair of trousers so tight across the crotch that they clearly reveal the swelling outline of your genitals.

The rock singers who have popularized this style are not as dumb as you may think they are. They know that, contrary to what scientists contended for years, most women are sexually excited by the sight of the penis, or by suggestive pumping of the hips, or other visual stimuli.

You can be sure her eyes will be drawn to the hard swell beneath your zipper, and as the evening advances, if you play your cards right, her eyes will be followed by her hands.

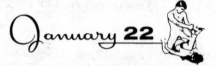

January 22

Try this technique as a part of cunnilingus. It will cause her to experience some of the most intense and powerful orgasms she has ever known.

While she still wears her panties and nylons, let your lips move down over her body, finally stopping when your face is directly over her thinly covered vulva. Cover her inner thighs with kisses, your tongue licking the sensitive flesh, and then let her feel the tip of your tongue trying to force its way under the elastic of her panties. Probe there with your tongue until you manage to touch the moist flesh of her vaginal lips.

Now place your open mouth over the very center of her crotch and suck gently but steadily for a moment. This will draw her clitoris out of the hood of flesh which conceals it, and you will know this has happened when she begins to squirm. That is when your tongue should begin to flicker with all the speed you can manage across the thin bit of silk that lies between it and her flesh.

The silk or nylon of her panties, moved across her clitoris by your rapidly flying tongue, will cause her to feel exquisite sensations she never knew existed; and when at last those panties are removed and she is naked beneath your mouth, each touch of your tongue will cause her to cry out the delight of another orgasm.

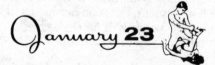

January 23

Try this variation of the male-above position for sexual intercourse, and show her how exciting this common position with a few twists can be!

As you assume your position above her and she lifts her legs to wrap them around your body, place one hand under her upper leg, lifting it

18

high as you enter her. Raise this leg until her knee is bent over your arm at the elbow, then shift your body forward, forcing her knee toward her shoulder, and hold it there as you drive your penis in and out of her.

After a few moments, release her leg, letting her place it lower around your body, and lift her other leg in the same manner. This shifting of her legs, and the turning of her lower body which it causes, allows your thrusting penis to make contact with various parts of her inner vagina—and that results in pleasure she never knew she could receive from this most ordinary of positions.

January 24

You are certainly aware that her breasts are among her most potent erogenous zones, but are you aware that her own hands can assist you as you use your lips and tongue to excite her?

Find out how tonight!

As you strip away her bra to reveal those naked globes of flesh, let her feel the warmth of your breath on her nipples, see the glow of pleasure on your face. Kiss the soft mounds a few times, letting your tongue tease her nipples to erection, and then take both her hands and place them under the delicious orbs, letting her know you want her to hold them for your mouth.

As she holds her breasts cupped and your lips tug and suck at her nipples, your hands stroking her naked flesh, her own touch will add to her arousal. Most women, when they masturbate (and you should know that almost all of them do), use manual stimulation of the breasts to increase their pleasure. And holding her breasts for you in this manner will also cause a vague stirring of her maternal instincts, which can be an important part of her feelings for you.

But you can safely bet she will display those feelings in a way that is far from maternal!

January 25

Walk boldly into the bathroom while she is in the tub!

Smile and ignore any weak protests she may make, and tell her that you came in to wash her back. Keep your promise, but follow it by letting your hands move around to slowly, sensuously wash her breasts, stomach, thighs, and finally, the soft hair and pink flesh of her pubis.

Help her out of the tub and use a soft, fluffy towel to rub her body dry, patting and gently scrubbing her breasts, thighs, and buttocks until they glow with warmth. Then let the towel fall to the floor and prepare yourself for the discovery of how much fun sex can be in a bathroom.

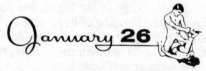

January 26

Take her to a club that features go-go dancers!

Not only is the atmosphere of these clubs meant to be intimate, the music sexual, but the sight of those nude, or nearly nude, dancers will arouse her competitive instincts. She will be inclined to show you that she can be just as sexy as these paid entertainers, and you can increase her desire to do this by a few teasing remarks about how aroused by the sight of all this nudity the other male patrons appear to be.

Then take her home and let her show you what true arousal can be!

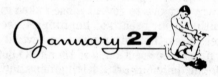

January 27

Use your own oral skills to encourage her to take you into her mouth and fellate you!

There are times when silence is truly golden, and, especially if she is shy about oralism, this is one of them. Say nothing about your own wishes as you strip away her clothing and guide her into a reclining position with her thighs parted and her vagina ready for your caresses. Let your body do the talking.

Use your tongue and lips on her clitoris until she begins to writhe with pleasure, then slowly turn, at first placing your naked body alongside hers, where her fingers can clutch at your hardness, and finally placing your lower body over her face, your penis conveniently dangling above her lips. She will know what you want, and not too many more strokes of your tongue will be required before you feel the warmth of her mouth covering your penis.

Even if she is an eager and experienced fellatrice, this classic position for simultaneous oral sex is one that will encourage her to new heights of endeavor, and she will be delighted at the way you made your request without asking.

Why not try it tonight?

January 28

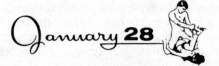

Go on a shopping trip that will pay dividends in the bedroom.

Visit the lingerie department in a large store, or go to a specialty shop that handles a wide variety of sexy undergarments. Buy her a pair of crotchless panties, a bra with openings for her nipples, and a short transparent gown to wear over them. Enclose a note telling her how sexy and beautiful you knew she would look in these items and ask her to think of you each time she wears them.

She will—and you will have the pleasure of seeing her wear them tonight!

January 29

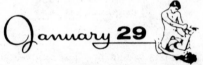

Here is a position that not only gives her the pleasure of feeling your hard penis slipping in and out of her vagina but also excites her by allowing her to watch most of the action.

When her panties have been stripped away and she is eager to feel the first thrust of your penis, have her lie on her back with her legs parted and her knees bent over the edge of the bed.

Standing between her legs, slip one hand under her buttocks and lift them high, throwing her weight back on her shoulders, as you insert your penis. When it is in and she is sighing with contentment, grasp her upper legs and lift them to a comfortable level around your body, then hold them there as your hips begin to pump.

This position causes an increased friction against her clitoris, and you will find her writhing in passion while her eyes watch, utterly fascinated, each stroke of your erected penis.

And wait till you see what the sight of her lovely, twisting body does for you!

January 30

Let her know the thrill of an anal caress combined with manual stimulation of her clitoris. It is one of the best ways of introducing her to the pleasures analism can provide.

Have her stand before you as you kneel to remove her panties, then lift your face to cover her vagina with your mouth. Use your tongue on her until she begins to move in a physical expression of her pleasure, then place your hands on her thighs and encourage her to turn around.

Now let your hands guide her into a bending position, as if you intended to perform cunnilingus from the rear, then press your face against her buttocks and let your tongue lick toward the flesh of her vaginal lips. Now reach around her with one hand, find the soft mound over her vagina, and move it in slow circles while your lips caress the naked flesh of her buttocks. Then use your free hand to spread those soft half-moons and send your tongue flickering swiftly over the circle of her anus—which, you should always remember, is as clean as any other part of her body and is not to be ignored if you wish to be the total lover she seeks.

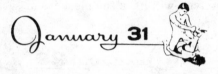

January 31

Let the energy crisis give a boost to your love life.

Take her for a ride in your car and head straight for the most deserted spot you know. As you travel this lonely road, switch off the ignition, then tell her you are out of gas; sigh with resignation, take her in your arms, and suggest that you make the best of a bad situation.

Wait until she is bubbling with eagerness before discovering that you have enough fuel to make it home to the bedroom—then go!

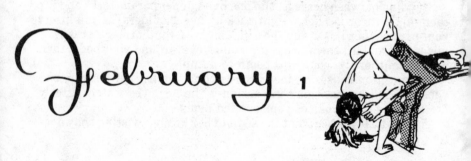

February 1

The classic position for simultaneous oral sex, often referred to as the "69" position, in which one partner lies over the other, is not always the best. It can be awkward for both and especially uncomfortable for the partner underneath. Here is a variation many lovers prefer. Why not try it tonight?

As you begin making love, turn beside her on the bed, your lips wandering from her breasts to her stomach to her inner thighs, and use your hands to encourage her to roll to one side, so she is facing your

hardened penis and your head rests comfortably between her upper legs.

As you begin to kiss and lick the moist flesh of her vagina, you will soon discover that this position encourages the slow, sensual rolling of her hips, and her reaction to the pleasure you are giving will be to take your penis between her lips and cling to it until it erupts and goes limp in her mouth.

February 2

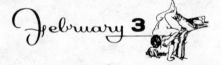

This is the day when, according to legend, the groundhog leaves his hole and predicts the weather by observing his shadow; so ask her to go groundhog hunting with you.

You may not even know what a groundhog looks like, and probably don't even care, but can you think of a better reason for inviting her into the nearest woods?

Once there, with the trees hiding you from view, take her into your arms, kiss her passionately, and let your hands go hunting across the softer curves of her body. She will cling so tightly to you, happily surprised at this turn of events, that any shadow the two of you cast will appear to be one.

And you can bet it will be a shadow that moves in the motions of love.

February 3

Is she sometimes—or often—reluctant to perform fellatio on you? If so, it may be because, like too many men, you have fallen into the habit of taking your own pleasure from this act while totally ignoring her own needs as a woman.

Tonight is the night to concentrate on filling those needs.

Use words of love and persuading hands to encourage her to take your penis into her mouth, and then, while she makes oral love to it, use your words and your caresses to make the act exciting to her.

Let your hands gently stroke her hair, the sides of her face, and the upper parts of her naked body, and show your appreciation of her skills by verbally expressing your pleasure. Describe, in exciting detail, the acts of love you intend to perform when her lips have released you. Then keep your promise!

Exhausted though you may be by the climax to which she brings you, you will find that your words and the taste of your flesh have made fellatio more exciting to her than ever before, and her eagerness should make it possible for you to maintain a state of hard readiness. Use it to satisfy the needs you have aroused in her and you will discover in the weeks ahead that fellatio has taken on a new appeal for her.

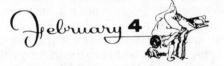

February 4

There are times when sex should be playful, strictly for fun, and here is a little sex game that will provide a lot of fun for the two of you. It is a real treasure hunt.

On small slips of paper have her list each item of her clothing, and you list yours on other slips. Now have her write down a sexual penalty you must pay if you lose, keeping it secret for the time being, and you write down a penalty for her.

Hide the slips listing your clothing in one room, and let her hide the ones listing hers in another. When this is done the two of you switch rooms and begin searching for the slips. When a hidden slip is located the other player must remove that item of clothing, and the first to become totally naked must then pay the penalty that was previously listed by the other.

An extra advantage of this game, you will find, is that the nudity makes the penalty easier to pay and paying the penalty is just as much fun as receiving it.

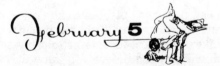

February 5

Many women enjoy a *tiny* bit of pain as they are making love, but the key to this lies in keeping the pain so mild that it is pleasurable and not harsh. And the pain gives sexual pleasure only when applied to certain specific areas of the human body.

Tonight, as you begin making love to her, try nipping gently with your teeth at the lobes of her ears, at her nipples, at the dimpled hollows on each of her inner thighs. Mix gentle kisses and the touch of your tongue in with these teasing bites, and pay careful attention to her bodily reactions. Discover the exact amount of pressure that is needed to give her pleasure, and in what parts of her body it is most effective, and you will soon have her thrashing beneath you as never before.

25

February 6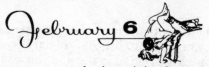

Call her while you are at work, thus giving her several hours to think it over, and casually announce that you have decided to be her slave for the night. Tell her that her every wish will be your command.

She will certainly have some surprises for you when you walk through the door, and only time can tell what they will be. You may find yourself bathing her, dressing her (or the opposite), or even dancing in the nude. But it will all be in fun, and you can bet that she will have planned a few chores for you to perform that will require all the sexual vigor you can muster.

Be a good slave and perform them well!

February 7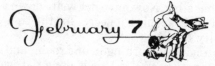

The proper position for anal sex can be just as important as in any other type of intercourse, and here is a position that is one of the best. Why not give it a try?

After a proper lubricant, such as Vaseline, or K-Y jelly has been applied to her anus (by you, in a way that will arouse her), lie flat on your back with your legs slightly parted and have her kneel between your thighs with her back to you. Lift your legs and place them over hers, so they lie across the backs of her knees, and she will be poised over the tip of your penis.

Either of you can part her buttocks as she eases herself down onto your erection, but your own hands should be softly caressing as you slide into her. Make no upward thrust until she has settled herself fully over you—which will happen before you know it.

This position, giving control of penetration to the female, will do away with most of the discomfort she may feel in ordinary anal penetration, and make the act far more enjoyable for her—which in turn makes it more enjoyable for you. Try it and see!

February 8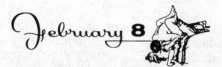

Try this way of making the man-above, or "missionary" position, more exciting for her—and reap the rewards of her twisting, writhing body as you make love!

As you move between her naked legs and prepare to enter her, put one hand high on each of her inner thighs and spread her legs as far as they will go without causing her discomfort, letting her fingers guide your erection to the waiting lips of her vagina.

Continue to press her thighs outward and upward, keeping the weight of your body off her, as you begin moving your penis in and out of her clinging loins, and you will soon make a delightful discovery: the manner in which you are pressing her thighs causes an automatic lifting of her pelvis, thus greatly increasing the pressure against her all-important clitoris. She will be in the seventh heaven of orgasm long before you reach your own climax.

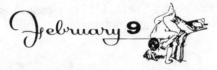

February 9

Wake her with your tongue!

Let her go to sleep, on the sofa or in the bed, and then very slowly and very quietly, being careful not to rouse her before you are in place, begin performing cunnilingus on her. Let your tongue lap very slowly and lovingly at her flesh, not flickering and darting as it normally would, and soon you will feel her fingers caressing the back of your neck.

Cunnilingus is more meaningful and far more exciting to the female when she believes her partner really enjoys what he is doing, and there is no better expression of your eagerness than letting her awaken to find you feasting on the flesh of her loins.

She will be quick to show you how pleased she is!

February 10

Take her "around the world"—without leaving your bed.

You probably know that the sexual experience referred to in slang as "around the world," or "a trip around the world," is a combination of fellatio, coitus, and anal intercourse, but has it occurred to you that she might enjoy being the recipient of a reverse version?

Tonight is the night to try it and see if she does.

Begin by using your tongue and lips on her vagina, lapping at her clitoris with skillful strokes, until her body goes taut with orgasm, and then guide her into the position for sexual intercourse that she most enjoys. By the time you reach your own climax the hard thrusting of your penis will have her in a state of almost continuous orgasm—and that is when you take her on the final part of her joyous "trip."

But not with anal intercourse, as you would do if she were giving you the opposite version of this experience; instead, while she still quivers with pleasure, guide her quickly over onto her stomach and lift her into a half-kneeling position, then kneel behind her and press your lips to her buttocks. Slip one arm around her, letting your hand find and manipulate the soft mound above her vagina, and then let your tongue find its way into the cleft between her buttocks. Flicker it back and forth over her anus.

Already shaken and trembling from repeated orgasm, she will quickly reach another, then another, as she feels your tongue touching her sensitive anus, your fingers manipulating her tormented clitoris, and don't be in the least surprised if her pleasure is so great that she wants to give you a "trip" of your own.

February 11

Take a shower or bath and create a situation that will arouse her no end!

After you have left the tub and dried yourself, knot the towel around your waist so that it barely covers your loins, then spend a moment or two creating erotic images in your mind. Dwell on these until you have an erection that is visible against the front of the towel, and then ask her to bring you some items you don't really need.

You can be sure she will notice the hard swell at the front of the towel (and remember, the sight or thought of the erected penis is sexually exciting to most females) and you can also be sure her hands will sneak beneath that towel as you kiss her deeply to thank her for the unwanted item she brought at your request.

Now you have only to untie the knot in the towel and show her what you've got.

February 12

Here is an exercise in sensuality. It is designed to make you a more effective lover when the two of you are using the female-above position for intercourse. Try it today and practice it with regularity.

Lie on your back with your arms lifted. Place your weight on your shoulders and heels, then lift your pelvis in a thrusting motion, exactly as you would do if she were above you. When your pelvis is lifted to its highest point, rotate your hips in slow circles before letting them fall. Repeat this as many times as you can, and plan on increasing the number of repetitions on future days; plan, also, on using these motions to drive her to ecstasy on future nights.

Would you like to buy her an item that makes the most sexually suggestive gift you can give? Of course you would, so why not buy it today.

Flavored douche powders—strawberry, raspberry, blueberry, and many others—are available at drugstores and through mail-order houses, and they make a gift that can suggest nothing but cunnilingus. Watch her eyes twinkle when she opens her gift to discover where your thoughts lie—and listen to her sighs of pleasure when, later, she gives you a real taste treat.

Valentine's Day

Valentine's Day—and it is a day that should be devoted to the romantic side of your relationship. She will be expecting some show of your feelings and will be ready to display her own, so why not try this small remembrance.

Take her, if possible, to the same place the two of you went on your first night together, or to the place where you spent an evening that lives in your memory. Try to recreate the atmosphere and events of that past evening, and let her know that it was a night you will never forget.

This night, you may be sure, will become another.

Make her come to you for cunnilingus!

Tonight, after you have stripped away her clothing and your hands and lips have stroked her naked breasts and thighs until she is straining and eager for sexual relief, slowly, your lips teasing every inch of her body, move down between her thighs, as if preparing to satisfy her with your lips and tongue.

Then delay that satisfaction for as long as you possibly can.

Now let your lips and tongue move teasingly over the dimpled hollows of her inner thighs (they are potent erogenous zones), let your breath play over the moist flesh of her vagina and the soft hair surrounding it, and lift your face to kiss the sleek flesh of her stomach; the idea is to let her feel your lips and tongue touching every spot but those which she most wants caressed, the clitoris and the vaginal lips.

As her hips begin to lift and weave, attempting to make contact with your teasing lips and tongue, withdraw until you are just out of reach and continue to caress her thighs. Put one hand over the soft mound above her vagina, thus adding to her arousal, and use it to maintain the distance between the two of you.

When at last her hands have grasped the back of your head and she is straining to draw you to the sweet cleft between her thighs, go slowly at first, letting your tongue dart forth to lick at her outer vaginal flesh, withdraw, and dart forth again. Then suddenly relent and use your lips and tongue to give her all the pleasure of which you are capable.

Her enjoyment will be doubled for having been so long denied.

February 16

Hide all her bras!

Wait till she is taking a shower, sneak into her room and steal her bras from their place of storage, then get your hands on any she may have taken into the bathroom. Wait for her to notice they are gone.

Deny all knowledge of the missing garments, but tell her she looks much better without them. Spend as much time as possible flattering the shape of her breasts before admitting that you did indeed hide the brassieres, and then use your hands, lips, and tongue to show her why.

She may never again wear a bra.

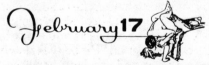

February 17

Try taking sex out of the bedroom tonight for a little added sparkle. A change of place is as good as a change of pace.

When you first arrive, sweep her into your arms, kiss her deeply, and let your eager hands find their way to the soft swells of her breasts, the taut curves of her buttocks, and the moist warmth that lies hidden beneath her skirt. If eagerness is evident in your every gesture, her desire will soon match your own.

When the twisting of her body and the heat of her kisses indicates she is ready for love, strip away her clothing and your own, letting her see the hard, erected expression of your desire, and make love to her in the nearest place that is suitable; this might be a sofa, a soft carpet, or in a standing position—but in any case it will be a satisfying and exciting way of varying your lovemaking.

February 18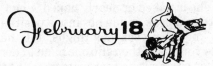

Ask her to share your pajamas with you!

Let her wear the tops, a perfect way for her to display her legs, buttocks, and perhaps a glimpse of pubic hair, while you wear the bottoms and reveal both a masculine chest and the ill-concealed erection caused by her scanty costume.

It will be no problem for you to unbutton the pajama tops and totally reveal those beautiful breasts of hers when you are ready to make love, but you are likely to find that she has beaten you to it by undoing the buttons of your pajama bottoms and reaching in to grasp your hard erection.

She will know how appealing she looks in her near-nudity, and that, it is safe to predict, will be tremendously exciting to her.

February 19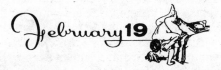

She will certainly enjoy this position, so why not introduce her to it this evening?

After using foreplay to arouse her to a point where she is able to wait no longer, and after removing her panties and bra, have her kneel with her legs slightly spread. You kneel behind her, your legs between hers, and stroke her body with your hands as you enter her from the rear.

When you are deep inside her and her body is slowly undulating, lean over her, reach beneath her and cup both her breasts in your hands, kneading them gently, and use the leverage your grip on her breasts provides to encourage her to rock back and forth on her knees and meet the thrusts of your erection.

This rear-entry position provides a high degree of friction against her clitoris, thus increasing her pleasure, and your hands on her breasts, your pubic hair teasing her buttocks, will make her enjoyment even greater. Try it and see.

February 20

Increase her desire for sex by delaying the first thrust of your penis—and see how exciting sex can be!

Tonight, when she is naked or nearly naked, when your foreplay has brought her desire to a peak, guide her into a position on her back, her legs parted, and kneel between her thighs. Lift her upper legs and drape them across your own, then slip one hand under her buttocks and raise them until her vagina is an inch or so from the tip of your erected penis.

Now grasp the shaft of your penis with your other hand. Touch it to her vaginal lips, pressing just enough to part them. Move it up and down between these soft folds of flesh, never letting it go deeper than an inch or so. Vary the speed with which you move it, sliding it slowly and then fast along the slit, and let her feel it touching her clitoris. When her own hips lift in an effort to gain the full length of your penis, swing your hips back, eluding her.

Soon her hand will clutch frantically at your own, fighting for the pleasure you are denying her; and when you plunge deep into her body and go into her arms, you will find she is a twisting, clawing, writhing bundle of pent-up desire. Satisfy her!

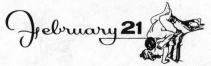

February 21

Let cunnilingus teach you an important fact about her sexuality.

Take her in your arms and kiss her deeply, letting your hands stroke her body to arouse her, and then indicate, with words or gestures, or simply by doing it, that you wish to perform cunnilingus.

When you are between her thighs and your caresses and the lapping of your tongue has brought the fleshy button of her clitoris to full erection (it does stiffen, you know, just like a tiny penis) draw this bit of flesh between your lips and, holding it there, begin to flick it back and forth, gently but fast, with the tip of your tongue—and mentally count the strokes. This is important.

As the lashing of your tongue brings her closer and closer to orgasm, and then to it, you may find her hands attempting to push you momentarily away from her pubis. This is because the clitoris, in some women, becomes extremely sensitive at the moment of orgasm. The touch of your tongue may even be painful. This moment soon passes, however, and you can then use your tongue to bring her to orgasm after orgasm—but you must know when to pause.

If she experiences no such moment, as many females do not, she will hold you to her at the moment of orgasm, and with a quicker flickering of your tongue you can sustain that orgasm for an incredible length of time.

Although other factors may.influence the exact number of strokes of the tongue required to bring her to orgasm, you will find that this number seldom varies greatly. And knowing the number will help you to perform future cunnilingus in a way that will greatly increase her pleasure.

So get her number tonight.

Stay in her arms long after making love—and the odds are good you will find yourself repeating the act!

Tonight, after you have finished making love, remain between her thighs, your penis still inside her, and cover her lips, face, and breasts with tender kisses while the swelling of your penis gradually subsides.

Not only is this display of affection important to any woman, a gesture that shows her that sex is not her only attraction, but it plays on a fact too many men do not know or, knowing it, ignore.

This fact is that the vaginal walls must expand to accept the erected penis and that as the erection fades, the vagina contracts around it. Unlike the sudden contraction caused by the abrupt withdrawal of the penis after intercourse, the slow shrinking of it inside the already tingling vagina causes a sensation of warmth that most women find delectable. So delectable, in fact, that her movements and caresses will soon be renewing the hardness of the erection you thought was gone.

Ask her to pose for some nude and semi-nude photos.

Most women, no matter what they may say, really do envy those girls who are paid to display their bodies—dancers, strippers, models, etc.—and she will be flattered if you go about this right.

Tell her she is far more lovely than most girls featured in such magazine photos, that you have long dreamed of seeing her in erotic poses and costumes, and assure her that no one else will see the pictures. You may be surprised at how readily she agrees, after a little coaxing.

Use a Polaroid to take the photos, and help her select the skimpy bras and undies she is to wear. Let your hands caress her body as you direct her poses—and be prepared to agree if she wants a few nude photos of you.

And be prepared for what will surely follow.

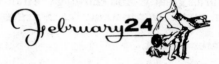

Buy an underground newspaper and leave it where she will be sure to see it.

The largest part of these publications, you will find, is the section containing the personal ads. These ads are placed by people seeking sexual partners of every sort, ranging from mate-swappers to those interested in group sex, to bondage enthusiasts and every bizarre form of sex known to man.

Though she is unlikely to answer these ads, and you would not want her to, they may very well arouse her and stimulate her imagination, for they cover the entire sexual spectrum.

And that arousal means a very enjoyable evening for *you*.

Here is an erogenous zone you should know. It is one you should never ignore when performing cunnilingus.

Tonight is the night to explore it.

Tonight, while she lies on her back with her thighs parted, bend low as if to lick her vagina, but pass over it and touch your tongue to the flesh that lies between the rear of her vagina and her anus. Let her feel the tip of your tongue licking her there, the flat of your tongue pressing this area, and when at last you do begin tasting her vagina you will find it already wet and ready for orgasm.

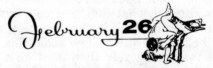

Is she reluctant to perform fellatio? If she is, it may well be because you have not done your best to help her shed the inhibitions caused by years of snickering verbal abuse society has directed toward those who engage in this perfectly natural act of love. You know the terms that have been used to describe those who perform fellatio, and the attitudes that have existed, so there is no need to go into that. Just show her that you hold none of these attitudes.

How?

Simply by using your normal means to encourage her to fellate you, and then, when she is through, whether she has brought you to climax or not, taking her in your arms and kissing her on the mouth. Not a peck, but a long kiss that sends your tongue probing into her mouth. There is nothing "dirty" about this; it is, after all, only a part of your body her lips have just released.

Enough said?

February 27

Try this bit of anal foreplay tonight.

When your kisses have brought her to a quivering state of passion and your hands have stripped away her outer garments, leaving her clad only in her bra and panties, stand and take her in your arms.

Still kissing her deeply, let your hands drift down to her buttocks and swing her hips forward, so she feels the hardness of your erection. Now let your hands gently ply the flesh of her buttocks, drawing them apart, pressing them together, and ease one finger into the cleft between them. Move the tip of this finger in a circular motion against her anus, pressing gently. Now, even more gently, try to insert it into her anus, drawing the nylon veil of her panties along with it; work the finger slowly and gently in and out of her rear. The nylon of her panties will make your finger more exciting to her than ever before, and soon the two of you will be hastily removing those panties to take advantage of that excitement.

February 28

Have a talk with her—about sex.

A prolonged discussion with her about all areas of sexuality is the best way to discover her likes and dislikes, and even her secret desires, but obvious as this may sound, it is something that few men do. Don't be one of those.

Begin the conversation by mentioning the subject of homosexuality and the Gay Liberation Movement. Ask how she feels about the subject, and then try to get her opinions on what behavior is "normal" and what is "abnormal."

You may be surprised to discover that her attitudes are far more liberal than your own, or they may not be, but in any case you will have gained access to her thoughts—and that will have future value.

February 29

If it's February 29th, this must be leap year, and this is the day upon which, according to tradition, it is proper for a woman to propose to a man.

Smile, give her a kiss, remind her of this grand old tradition, and tell her you will quite happily do anything she proposes.

She will make this an interesting night for you.

March 1

You may not be able to add excitement to your love-making by covering the ceiling of your bedroom with mirrors, as many wealthy people do, but you probably have a full-length mirror in your bath which can be used to give her the same thrill.

So give her that thrill tonight.

Wait until she has stepped out of the shower, then enter the bathroom and quickly take her in your arms. After a lengthy kiss turn her so her back is to you and she is facing her reflected image as you cover her bare neck and shoulders with kisses and fondle her breasts with your hands.

Let her feel your erection against her rear as you continue to kiss her earlobes and the hollow of her throat, and expect to feel her shiver with delight as her eyes stare into the mirror, entranced by the sight of the hand now moving down to manipulate her clitoris.

Women as well as men are subject to arousal by visual stimuli, as you will discover when you try this, and this is but one of many ways in which a mirror may be used to increase her sexual excitement.

March 2

You are no doubt aware that those massage parlors which cater to men (at least some of them) offer much more than a massage, but did you know that other parlors are now offering similar services to women? And that they are growing extremely popular?

Find out why they are so popular—tonight!

Use one of those battery-powered vibrators (they are not very expensive and are a valuable sexual aid) that is designed to strap on the back of the hand and have her remove her clothing while you give her a massage.

Let your fingers move constantly over her breasts, buttocks, anus, and the soft clitorial mound above her vagina, and soon she will be ready to explode with orgasm. She is then ready for the grand finale.

Use the hand wearing the vibrator to press down on the soft rise of her pubis, letting her feel the pulsations deep within her flesh, and then use your teasing, lapping tongue to drive her to the height of ecstasy.

She will remember that orgasm for as long as she lives.

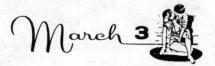

March 3

On this day in 1939 a man named Lothrop Withington, Jr., started a national fad by swallowing a three-inch goldfish in order to win a ten-dollar bet.

Commemorate this historic event by arriving with a goldfish in a bowl beneath your arm, recounting for her what Lothrop Withington, Jr., did, and telling her you mean to celebrate by eating it.

When she expresses her disbelief, set the bowl on a table, take her in your arms, and smile as you remind her that you said not a single word about eating the fish.

Then celebrate!

March 4

Buy her a copy of *The Woman's Perpetual Love Calendar*, the companion book in this series. She will love you for it.

Not only does it offer daily suggestions that will help to improve her sexual techniques, thus making sex more enjoyable for the pair of you, but it is filled with tips that will help her to overcome any inhibitions she may have and information that will help her reach a better understanding of both male and female sexuality.

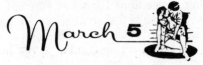

Tonight let a bottle of baby oil add a new sheen to your lovemaking!

Have the bottle of lotion near the bed, and at the proper moment, when she is naked and ready, pour a few drops of it into the palm of your hand and ask her to relax while you apply it to her body. Do this with gentle, arousing strokes of your hand; and then, when her body is gleaming with the smooth oil, lie back and let her spread it over you.

Both of you will enjoy the process of applying the oil, but more important, you will find that there is an exciting new sleekness of your bodies as you come together for the making of love.

No baby ever had it so good.

Here is a position for sexual intercourse that causes maximum pressure against the clitoris, thus making it extremely pleasurable for the female, and she will love you for introducing her to it.

So make that introduction tonight!

Have her lie on her back on the bed while you stand ready between her parted thighs. Slip one hand under her buttocks, or both hands under her thighs, and swing her hips up to meet your penis. This will throw most of her weight back on her shoulders, and you will feel her legs locking around your naked back.

Though you will be partially supporting her with your hands as your penis begins slipping in and out of her vagina, the weight of her own body will cause her clitoris to remain in constant contact with the hard shaft of your penis.

And that means she will be hot and wet with orgasm long before you have reached your own climax.

Is she hesitant to try anal intercourse because she feels it might be painful? Or because she doubts that it would prove pleasurable for her?

Then use one of those small, battery-operated penis-shaped vibrators (available at most drugstores, if she doesn't own one) to show her how pleasant it can be.

After securing her agreement for what you are about to attempt, have her remove her panties and assume a kneeling position. Cover the vibrator with a thin film of Vaseline or K-Y jelly, apply a bit of the same to her anus, and be especially gentle as you let her feel the first touch of the humming instrument.

Let your free hand be gently caressing her naked breasts, buttocks, or pubic mound, as you tenderly place the vibrator in the cleft between her buttocks, and allow her time to relax and grow accustomed to its feel before pressing it against the anal entry.

Continue to caress her naked body with your lips and hands as you gently but steadily slide the vibrator into her anus; it should go easily and without pain, for it is the proper size and slippery in its own right. Now let her feel it moving in and out of her anus, and watch for the glow of desire that will spread over her face.

Even if she has strong anal desires, even if anal intercourse is a steady part of your sexual relationship, this technique is one you will want to try, for that buzzing vibrator, when at last it is withdrawn, will leave a tingling vacancy she will want you to fill.

March 8

Do a striptease act for her.

Does that sound a bit silly to you? It won't to her. Not really. Nudity, you see, can be just as exciting to the female as to the male, contrary to what most people once thought.

So make the offer lightly, teasingly, and see how quickly she takes you up on it. Dim the lights, let her make herself comfortable, and go ahead with your act. You will probably find her reaching out to help you as you remove the last of your garments, her fingers brushing your naked body.

That means it is time to go into your encore.

March 9

Here is an exercise in sensuality. Try it today and practice it often, for it can greatly increase your effectiveness as a lover.

Thrust your tongue out as far as it will go, then slide it back into your mouth as far as you can. Do this twenty times today and try to work up to fifty in future attempts.

Its ultimate purpose should be obvious.

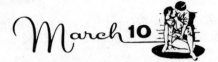

March 10

You know that it is important to use various positions for sexual intercourse, but has it occurred to you that cunnilingus can be made more exciting in the same way? Here is a position that will greatly enhance your oral lovemaking.

Take her in your arms while standing and use passionate kisses and even more passionate touches of your hands to arouse her to readiness, then slowly drop to your knees before her, leaving a trail of kisses in your wake, and ease her panties down to the floor.

Touch your lips lovingly to the soft fur of her pubes, then place both arms between her thighs, turn your palms to cradle the rounded curves of her buttocks, and urge her to swivel her pelvis forward. Let your lapping tongue greet her vagina as she does.

Now, while your tongue dips into the pink and coral flesh between her vaginal lips, let your hands knead the flesh of her buttocks, and, as she begins to respond to the touch of your lips and tongue, use your grip on her rear to urge her to swing her hips to and fro; she will soon pick up this motion on her own, and her wet and hot vulva will be thrusting eagerly against your face as her legs begin to tremble.

Better have a bed behind her, as she is going to need something to fall back on . . . taking you with her.

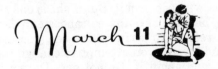

March 11

Swap "dirty" jokes with her, the so-called "blue" jokes that people tell at parties. Few women are offended by these, and, quite to the contrary, you may discover she knows more jokes than you.

Begin by telling her the latest one you have heard and daring her to top it, then continue until you have exhausted your supply of jokes. And remember that there is a point in all this; aside from the fact that it will tend to make your conversation more frank, open, and relaxed, any psychologist will tell you that you can learn a great deal about a person from the type of jokes he or she enjoys.

March 12

Use the female-above position for sexual intercourse to show her how incredibly deep your penetration of her vagina can be . . . and how incredibly wonderful it can feel.

After you have removed her panties and are ready to make love, roll onto your back, drawing her over you, and place your legs close together as she straddles your hips. Keep your lips to hers, your hands caressing her naked back, breasts and buttocks as you thrust your erected penis into her, and draw your feet up so you will have leverage for what you are about to do.

With your weight now on your feet and shoulders begin to pump your hips upward, and then, as she begins to react with excited undulations of her own body, lift your pelvis high, so she is actually lifted and suspended over your erection. Use your hands on her buttocks to exert downward pressure for a moment, while your hips move in slow circles that grind your groin against hers.

When using the female-dominant position it is very important that you make a conscious effort to exert pressure against her clitoris, and this technique is one that exerts such pressure to the extent that she will soon be clawing at your body as she sighs with satisfaction.

March 13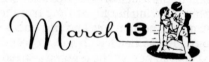

Fellatio is a form of sex that most women today readily accept as a natural part of the male-female relationship, and it is a source of pleasure to most who perform it. But if she is one of the few remaining females who, because of outdated taboos and deeply held but incorrect prejudices, refuses to perform oral sex, you will need to display both patience and love as you attempt to change the situation.

Do not argue about it. Do not nag. Do not insist. Any act of love should be engaged in only by mutual consent—and there is the best way to overcome her prejudices.

Tonight, as you begin to make love, as your kisses and caresses are bringing her passion to a peak, ask her to use her lips and tongue on your nipples and stomach. She is probably aware of these erogenous zones, but if not, she is going to be pleased by your reaction as she explores them. Continue to kiss and caress her body as she does, including her vagina, if she turns so it is accessible. Your penis is readily available if suddenly she decides to taste it, but for tonight be content with what she freely offers. Some time may pass before she surprises you by grasping it and taking it in her mouth to suck it for the first time, but you have started her on the path by having her orally explore other parts of your body. Most experienced fellatrices began in some way similar to this.

And even if she is an eager and experienced fellatrice, even if fellatio is a major ingredient in your sexual diet, the time spent on this will not be wasted, for those few moments will make the ultimate act more enjoyable for each of you.

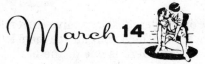

The silky feel of her nylons, panties, and bra are, of course, very exciting against your naked skin, but have you given thought to the many ways in which various materials can be used to increase *her* enjoyment of the sex act?

Try this one tonight.

Cover the bed with a spread of synthetic fur, or a blanket made of the softest, most fluffy material you can find. Holding it against your face for a moment will give you a good idea of how it is going to feel against her naked skin.

And be sure she is naked as you begin to make love. Let her feel that delicious and exciting softness against her back and buttocks as she writhes beneath you. You can be sure it will give added pleasure to each thrust of your hardened penis.

Combine tenderness and strength to make your loving something she will remember—and want to feel repeated.

Tenderness and strength are probably the two characteristics most women would like a man to have, yet few men seem capable of both. You are not one of those who are lacking.

Tonight let your sexual foreplay be more tender than ever before, with your hands and lips bestowing the most gentle of caresses on her face, throat, breasts, thighs, and stomach; indeed, on every last inch of her body.

Then let your lovemaking be ferocious.

With her breasts or buttocks clutched tightly in your hands, your teeth closing on her throat or nipple, drive your erected penis at her with hard, pounding strokes that cause naked skin to slap against naked skin. Let her feel your full strength with each driving thrust you make; and then, when it is over, once again use your lips and hands to show her how tender you can be.

It makes a contrast she will love.

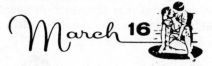

Her nipples are one of her most explosive erogenous zones, and there are many, many ways in which you can use them to increase her enjoyment during copulation. Here is one of the best.

As you begin to make love, when your penis is in her and her legs are locked around your waist, cover the tip of her breast with your mouth and gently suck the nipple between your lips. Hold it there, teasing it with your tongue, during the first moments of intercourse, until the pace begins to quicken, building toward orgasm.

Then at regular intervals thrust your penis deep into the warm wetness of her vagina and hold it there, your upper groin grinding against her clitoral mound, and at the same time, holding her nipple between your lips, flick your tongue rapidly over the stiffened tip. When you draw your penis back to resume the movements of your hips, let your tongue cease flicking her nipple. Let it resume the next time you bury the full length of your penis in her.

Just don't expect to repeat this combination many times, for it will soon have her writhing in orgasm, and the delightful twisting of her hips will have you following close behind.

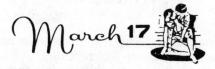

Saint Patrick's Day.

Buy her a pair of green panties, matching bra and garter belt, and nylons, all in a shade that will go well with the coloring of her hair and skin. As you give them to her, remind her of the tradition of wearing green on this day, and ask her to wear them.

Then walk into the bedroom as she is changing, and grin as you tell her you could think of no other way to confirm that she was really putting them on.

Play this right and she will take them off before you know it.

March 18

Teasingly dare her to rape you.

You may be surprised at how quickly she accepts this challenge. One of the more common sexual fantasies among females is one in which they imagine themselves as overpowering a sexually attractive but reluctant male and forcing him to cater to their sexual whims.

Make it all teasing, a joke, and offer just enough resistance to force her to struggle a bit. Make her do the work of removing your clothes, resisting slightly.

Then relax and let yourself be ravaged.

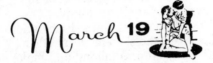

March 19

Here is a technique that actually combines three positions for intercourse, and just as it triples the usual number of positions, it will also triple the pleasure.

So you will surely want to try it tonight.

When first you begin making love have her take the female-above position, so she is astride your penis and her legs are on the outside of your own. Use this position until her hips begin to churn above you, and then, drawing her down and locking your lips to hers, roll to one side. With your hips pumping between her thighs and your tongue probing her mouth, use this until the heated movements of her body tell you she is nearing orgasm, then roll again and place yourself above her, thusting deep and bringing her to orgasm.

Each time you roll in this technique you are causing your penis, at least momentarily, to change its angle of penetration, thus exerting pressure against various parts of her vagina. Penetration may also be greater for brief instants . . . and these things add up to sex at its very, very best.

March 20

Do you recall those so-called "passion marks" that boys and girls gave one another during heated sessions of petting? You have probably had—and given—a few yourself, and might recall that they are a bruise made by closing the teeth tightly but not painfully over a tender

area and then sucking hard until the skin reddens. They cause a somewhat pleasurable tingling that may last for days.

Use this technique to give her a lasting reminder of what an incredible lover you are, and do it tonight.

Kiss and caress her body in a way that makes it clearly evident that
you intend to perform cunnilingus on her, your lips moving ever closer
to the sweet delicacy that lies between her thighs and your hands
guiding her to a position that will easily allow you to lay your head between the sleek columns of her upper legs.

When at last you are between those parted thighs and the sweet
scent of her loins surrounds you, place your lips against one thigh, at
least halfway down, and use the techniques described above to place a
"passion mark" on the smooth skin. Place another on the opposite
thigh, at the same level, and then move a little higher. Use one hand to
massage her soft furry clitoral mound and make her brief wait more
bearable as you create a trail of these marks that will end only when
your lips are caressed by the feathery hair and delicate flesh of her
vagina.

You will then find that the trail you left is one she is often going to
want you to follow.

March 21

Turn her over your knee and tell her you're going to give her a
spanking!

Approach this playfully, all in good fun, but pretend that the spanking is punishment for some infraction she has committed, even if
imaginary. Tell her the reason she is going to be spanked, laugh away
her objections, and bend her over your lap. Pull up her skirt, tug down
her panties and, without inflicting real pain, give her a few slaps that
will make her bare bottom sting.

Don't be surprised to find that the slapping of your hand against the
curves of her rump causes her to become suddenly and amazingly
aroused, as spanking is a form of sexual foreplay used and enjoyed by a
great many couples. It is filled with erotic meaning. But even if she is
not aroused by the mild pain inflicted by your open hand, she will be
when you take her in your arms and use that same hand to rub away
the sting.

Either way, you can't lose.

March 22

You are reading this book because you want to be a more satisfying lover, and she also wants to know that she is totally satisfying to you. You can use these simple facts to make the relationship better for both of you.

As you make love tonight, simply tell her, over and over, what a wonderful partner she is. Try to describe the joy she gives you with each of her own personal techniques, the sensations you feel when your penis is held tightly by her weaving vagina, the delight you find in the feel and the taste of her breasts.

These words are extremely exciting to a woman, and you will happily discover that she responds by seeking new ways to lift your opinion even higher. This is one of those cases where what you say is almost as important as what you do.

So speak to her with words of love.

March 23

Take her horseback riding.

There are stables in all areas where horses may be rented, most of them with wooded trails for riding and secluded areas for picnics, and the brisk weather of spring is the best time to enjoy the privacy and companionship of the sport. Intimate moments may be shared in beautiful surroundings, and, if she is among the large number of women who experience a vague sense of sexual arousal as she straddles the rocking, swaying saddle, moments of a far more intimate nature will be yours to enjoy when you return to your home.

March 24

Here is a position that may very well become her favorite, so why not try it tonight?

When she is ready and eager for love strip away her panties and have her lie on her back while you kneel between her parted thighs.

Slip one hand under her buttocks and lift them high off the bed as you use your other hand to guide your penis to her waiting vagina, and continue to hold her in this position until you are settled deep inside her.

Now lift one of her legs until it points almost straight up, let her ankle fall across your shoulder, and then do the same with her other leg. Her lower body will be lifted high and you will have to give her support by keeping your hands under her back or buttocks, but the pleasure for both of you will be well worth the effort.

March 25

Make a contest of your lovemaking.

Dare her to see who can remain motionless the longest while your erected penis is inside her, and agree upon a sexual penalty the loser must pay.

The best position to use for this is one in which you lie on your back while she kneels astride your erected penis, facing you, as this will allow each of you to stroke and fondle the naked body of the other in your efforts to incite movement.

And don't be afraid to "lose" this one, because that is when the fun really begins.

March 26

Give her breakfast in bed.

It is one of the most meaningful gestures you can make, it requires very little cooking skill and even less time, and it will surely add a great deal to your relationship.

And she will probably ask you to join her.

But not for breakfast.

March 27

Hide the bathroom towels.

When she takes her shower and discovers their absence, she will be forced to ask you to bring her one. And when she makes this request, you can hold the towel just out of reach and teasingly demand that she come out after it. She will, sooner or later, and you can make amends by using the towel to rub her naked body until she is dry and glowing.

And the act of love that follows will leave the two of you in need of a shower that you can enjoy together.

Here is a unique variation of rear-entry intercourse that is really exciting to most females. Since it offers equal pleasure to the male, you will not want to let this night go past without giving it a try.

When she is hot, naked, and willing, have her assume a kneeling position on the bed. You kneel behind her, with your legs folded under you, so your buttocks are resting against your heels, your knees together and between her lower legs.

Now put your hands on her waist and urge her back and down, onto the shaft of your erected penis, so the soft curves of her buttocks are nestled in your lap. With your arms around her and your hands fondling her breasts and clitoral mound you can give her added pleasure while assisting her in the movements that slide her vagina up and down the length of your penis. And since her legs are on the outside of yours, you can, by moving your knees wider apart, cause her legs to spread, which in turn changes the degree and angle of penetration. Do this over and over, and soon you will feel the hot warmth of her orgasmic juices flowing around your penis.

This is a somewhat sneaky way of stirring her sexual desires, but you can make up for your sneakiness later by being a tender and satisfying lover.

Be seated in a comfortable chair and, as she walks past, catch her by the wrist and draw her toward you. Extend one of your legs so it is between hers, use your hands on her waist or hips to draw her down so she sits astride it, and quickly pull her close for a long and passionate kiss.

While your tongue searches her mouth and your hand caresses her breasts, bounce your knee up and down gently, very gently, because your thigh will now be against her crotch. Use your hand on her waist to move her hips to and fro, which will create the same sensations she might feel if masturbating, and use your thigh to maintain constant pressure on the softness of her clitoral region. Soon you will feel her hips gently pumping of their own will, and that means it is time for you to repay her for your sneakiness.

Do so with the coin of love.

March 30

Positions for oral sex are limited only by the imagination, but it requires little imagination to see that the following position is one of the very best for cunnilingus. Why not give it a try?

Have her lie on one side while you lie between her legs, placing yourself so your arm is holding her leg across your upper ribs. This will place your face within inches of her buttocks and her parted vagina, and as you move to caress her, you will discover that not only are you able to lap, lick, and suck at her vagina, but with very little effort you can give the same attention to her buttocks and the sensitive cleft that lies between.

It is impossible to say which she will enjoy most.

March 31

Ask her to join you for a walk in the moonlight.

This is the time of year when romance is in the air, and while that may or may not sound important to you, you should remember that few women will want to continue a relationship in which the romance is lacking.

So take her for a walk in the nearest place that is scenic. Let her feel your arm around her waist, your lips touching hers, and let her hear you whispering words of love.

You will discover that your romantic mood is highly contagious.

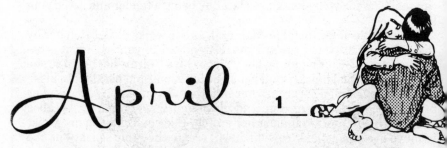

April 1

A little bit of jealousy is sometimes good for a relationship, so take this opportunity to teasingly arouse her jealousy.

Be a little bit late in arriving, and have a tiny smudge of lipstick on your collar, one or two strands of hair clinging to the sleeve of your coat, and, perhaps, a smudge of makeup on your underwear.

Let her discover these. Then, before she has a chance to say something she might later regret, grin and remind her of the date.

April Fools' Day!

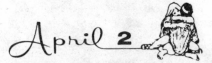

April 2

Give her what many feel is the most thrilling of all anal experiences—"the seven knots of heaven," or, as it is sometimes called, "the handkerchief of love." It is an ancient method of providing anal stimulation, is well known among the most skilled of lovers, and was mentioned in the play *Lenny* about the life of Lenny Bruce.

Use a fine silk scarf and roll it into a cord. Tie several knots in the cord (seven is the usual number, for reasons unknown) and insert the cord into her anus. Leave it there while you have sexual intercourse, or while you perform cunnilingus on her.

As she approaches orgasm, tug steadily on the cord, bringing one or two of the knots free of her anus, and as she begins to have her first orgasm, suddenly pull the entire cord free. This causes a hard, sustained orgasm that will leave her trembling and eager for more.

This works equally well when it is reversed and the scarf is inserted into the man's anus, so don't object if she wants to give that a try. Just relax and enjoy it.

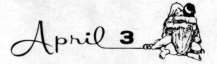

April 3

Take her to see the sexiest movie in town!

Women are just as stimulated by the sight of nudity and sex as men are, and the theaters showing R- and X-rated movies have come a long way in recent years; no longer are such films confined to rat-infested fire-traps; these films are now shown in theaters that are clean and well-kept and, in some cases, even plush. You will find many couples and unescorted females among the patrons.

And you will find her excitement increasing with each erotic scene that unfolds on the screen, perhaps to the extent that her hand moves in the darkness to explore the hard evidence of your own excitement.

Take her home for the second feature.

April 4

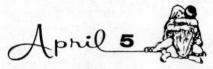

Here is an exercise in sensuality that will allow you to make more effective use of your tongue when caressing her nipples, navel, buttocks, and yes, even her vagina. Start doing it today and practice it regularly.

Extend the tongue fully and move it in a sweeping clockwise circle, flick it up and down about five times, and then move it in the counterclockwise direction. Repeat this about twenty times, varying the speed with which you move the tongue, and get in a little extra practice tonight when you are with her.

April 5

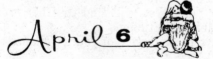

You know how your own excitement is increased by the feel of her naked breasts against your chest, her bare buttocks writhing in your hands, or the soft flax of her pubic hair teasing your skin; but are you aware that your own masculine flesh is just as exciting to her?

Prolonged contact is the idea for tonight.

As you kiss her lips and explore her mouth with your tongue, deliberately move your hardened penis against her. Let her feel it touching her naked inner thighs, her stomach, any part of her body you can reach. And prolong the foreplay so that you reach as many as possible. If you perform cunnilingus—and that is usually a good idea—turn slowly as you begin to do so and let her feel the tip of your erection or your testicles brushing her ribs, breasts, or even her face. Place her hand on it as you lap the delicious juices from her vagina. You will soon discover that this prolonged contact makes her even more eager to feel the warm glow of your penis prodding deep into her vagina.

And that is the best contact of all.

April 6

Buy her the shortest micro-mini you can find, one that will barely cover the curves of her buttocks, and tell her you were unable to pass it by because you realized how exciting she would look wearing it. Use a lot of flattery as you give it to her, telling her the curves of her legs and bottom are too good to be hidden—and then talk her into wearing it about the house with nothing beneath it!

This will be much easier than you might think.

There is a bit of the exhibitionist in all of us, and she will be pleased to know that you are so excited by her body that you went out of your way to have her display it at its alluring best; and, of course, she will be fully aware of your ultimate goal.

Wait a bit before attempting to reach that goal. Spend a little time commenting on her tempting loveliness, using the gleam in your eye and an occasional pat of your hand to stimulate her, and then let her revel in the feel of what her near-nakedness has done to you. For this she need not even remove the micro-mini.

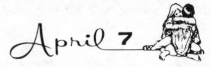

April 7

Use your fingers to bring her to orgasm . . . before you begin sexual intercourse. It will have her reaching renewed orgasm with each thrust of your penis.

When you have removed her panties and bra, and you, yourself, are naked, have her lie back against the pillow while you continue to kiss her lips and suck her nipples. Urge her thighs apart and, spreading the fingers like a fan, place one hand over her mons, that soft, yielding mound above her vagina. Use your fingers to move this in slow, sensuous circles, varying the pressure until her hips begin to weave. Let your kisses grow more passionate and demanding as you do this.

As she becomes more and more aroused, as your fingers cause her desire to grow, she will, of course, through words, gestures, or both, plead with you to give her the relief that only your penis can give. Put this off as long as possible by telling her it is going to be all the better for waiting . . . and if you're working it right, it will.

For soon the expert manipulations of your fingers, combined with the arousing caresses of your lips and tongue, and the further stimulation she will provide as she reacts with an ever faster rolling of her hips, will have her wet with the juices of orgasm.

And when at last you enter her and her hips lift her vagina to greedily swallow your penis, you will find that her orgasms are violent, explosive, and almost continuous.

So why not give those fingers of yours a chance to show what they can do?

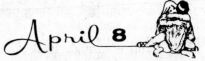

April 8

Use a little frustration to make her crave your penis as never before. She will take out these frustrations on you.

54

Tonight, as you begin to make love, urge her to take any of the female-dominant positions, and then wait until she is settled over your penis and the pumping of her hips reveals her heated passion before taking the next step.

Now slip one hand between your bodies and, waiting until her hips are lifted and only the tip of your penis remains within her, make a fist around the shaft of your erection, thus denying her its full length. Continue to kiss and suck her breasts, to caress her naked buttocks with your other hand, as she strains to regain the inches of flesh your fist now denies her.

She will soon reach down to tear away those obstructing fingers, or coax you into removing them, and when you do, you will find that she is hot and eager for every last inch of your flesh—and maybe even a little more.

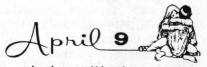

April 9

Fantasy plays a part in the sex life of every person, male or female, and you can greatly increase her sexual pleasure by encouraging her to fantasize while you perform cunnilingus on her, or while you cover her body and drive your penis rapidly in and out of her lifting vagina. But use a cautious approach.

Tell her you have been reading an article describing how most people use fantasy to increase sexual pleasure, admit that you do the same, and tell her that tonight, while you are making love, you want her to fantasize freely; but don't, whatever you do, ask her to describe these fantasies. She may well decide to do so of her own free will, but it is more probable that she will feel they are too bizarre and be reluctant to talk about them. But you can bet that your encouragement will cause her to fantasize, and react, as never before.

She may have visions of being raped and ravaged, as many women do, or she may imagine herself in bed with another man, or taking part in group sex—all common fantasies—but it will be you who enjoys the pleasure of her frantic and delightful loving.

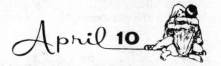

April 10

Challenge her to a little game of sexual "Beat the Clock."

Set a time limit of about two minutes and use an alarm to enforce it. Be naked and give her the first turn as she attempts, using whatever means she may desire, to bring you to a climax before the time limit expires. Then reset the timer and see if you can bring her to orgasm before the time is up. Set a sexual penalty for each failure, and soon the two of you will be having far too much fun to bother resetting the clock.

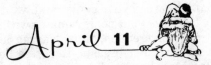

April **11**

Do you always perform cunnilingus by approaching her from the front? If so, you are denying both of you the added pleasure this act can give when done in any of a variety of ways. Here is one she will love you for trying.

When she is naked, and her hands, lips, and writhing body tell you she is ready to be loved, use your gently caressing hands to turn her over onto her stomach, as if you were preparing to enter her from behind and above. Use softly stroking hands to spread her thighs wide and then quickly straddle her naked body, facing her feet and with your hardened erection touching her naked back. Slip one hand under her mons and urge her to lift her hips slightly as you bend down and seek her vagina with your mouth.

This position allows you not only to suck and lick at the dewy lips of her vagina but also literally begs you to do the same to the buttocks pressing against your face and the sexually sensitive anus which lies between them. This is as clean as any other part of her body, so don't hesitate to explore it. It will add even more to the tremendous pleasure she is already experiencing.

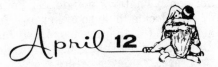

April **12**

Here is a rear-entry position for sexual intercourse that is so enjoyable it may very well become both her favorite and yours, and tonight is the night to give it a try.

Often referred to as "spoon-fashion," this method is especially pleasing because of the way it allows her to feel your pubic hair teasing her buttocks with each stroke of your penis, the full length of your naked body against her back, and your hands cradling her breasts while your lips caress her shoulders or neck.

Simply have her lie on her side, with one leg slightly lifted and her naked buttocks filling the hollow of your groin as you lie behind her and guide your penis to its delectable resting place. Let your hands roam her naked flesh while your penis begins to move, and add further spice to your loving by guiding one of her hands down to the furry little rise above her vagina. She will know what to do with it, and the resulting twists of her body will soon have the two of you straining together in orgasm.

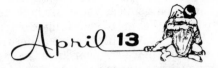

April 13

Does it excite you to imagine yourself greedily lapping wine or other drink from the deepest recesses of her vagina? Or having her tongue lick the same way from your hard and erected penis. Well, you are not alone. This desire is fairly common among men and not really rare among women. She will probably enjoy it and take an active part in the fun if you approach it properly.

Take a bottle of wine and two glasses to bed with you, wait until she is relaxed, then playfully pour a few drops onto her body and lick them away. Repeat this, moving closer to her vagina, and then pour a few drops on your body. Smile as you ask her to lick them away. And don't be surprised if, after a bit, she is taking her wine from the shaft of your hardened penis, or holding the bottle tilted so a steady stream of it flows across her vagina into your waiting mouth.

Better have a second bottle handy.

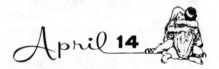

April 14

Tickle her . . . and tickle her fancy!

Catch her when she least expects it, get her in a grip from which she can't escape, and tickle her until she bursts into laughter. Then release her for a moment and go after her once again.

Most women love this sort of playful roughhousing, and she will make every effort to overpower you with a few well-placed tickles of her own. The body contact resulting from this is certain to lead to touches of a far more intimate nature, and those touches will lead to a spur-of-the-moment bout of lovemaking which will be nothing to laugh about. Not that it won't be fun.

April 15

Some of the greatest positions for sexual intercourse are the ones which are most comfortable, and this is equally true of positions for oral sex. She will be far more delighted by the way your mouth kisses her vagina and your tongue licks her clitoris if she is in a relaxed position that makes no distracting demands on her body.

Here is such a position. Why not try it tonight?

Let her be reclining on a sofa as you begin making love, and wait until she is eager to feel the licking of your tongue before slipping her panties down over her ankles. Now lift the one of her feet that is closest to the back of the sofa and place it so her knee is bent and her lower leg rests comfortably along the upper edge of the couch. Her parted legs will clearly reveal the delectable treat that awaits your tasting.

Your position will be dictated by the size and shape of the sofa. You may want to sit beside her, with her hand clutching your erected penis, while you bend down to lap her vagina from above; or you may prefer to kneel beside the sofa and place your head between her thighs, licking her from a more frontal position; in either case, you will surely find her hands caressing you, her hot juices flowing, as her reclining position allows her to fully enjoy the luxurious warmth provided by your adoring lips and tongue.

And you will soon feel her attempting to draw your body up over hers on the sofa. Make yourself comfortable.

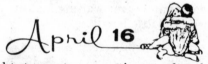

$\mathcal{A}$pril 16

Use your thoughts to create an erection—and see how it arouses her!

Without saying a word, stare hard at her breasts, trying to imagine them totally naked, recalling their taste. Let your eyes wander to the juncture of her thighs, and use the tip of your tongue to wet your lips. Remaining silent, try to create vivid mental images of the best sexual interlude you and she have shared.

The general direction of your thoughts will soon become evident, as will your arousal, and you will begin to see the first signs of her own arousal: stiffening nipples, perhaps, or a slow, tempting smile.

Such a method of staring is usually arousing to the female, especially when done by one she loves, and when you stand to reveal the bulge of the erection you have created with your erotic thoughts, you will almost certainly find that she wants to do more than look at it. Let her.

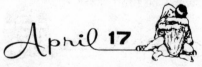

$\mathcal{A}$pril 17

Here is a sexual technique that can enhance the enjoyment found in any sexual position, though it is easiest to manage if you kneel above her with her legs parted and around your waist. It allows her to enjoy not only the feel of your hardened erection slipping deep into her vagina but the added pleasure of having it pass through her circling fingers—and that will double the pleasure for you as well. Find out about it tonight.

As you half-kneel between those warm thighs and slip your penis into her moist vagina, take one of her hands in your own. Guide it down between her thighs and use your fingers to close hers very lightly around the exposed shaft of your penis. Now begin slowly pumping your hips, letting your penis glide in and out, and you will begin to see that her pleasure is increased merely by the added contact. She may also lift slightly upward on the moving shaft, thus increasing the pleasure-giving friction against her clitoris, but of one thing you may be certain: she will get her fingers out of the way and claw wildly at your back or buttocks when her excitement becomes so great that she can go no longer continue without feeling the full length of your throbbing penis.

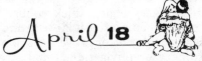

April 18

Ask her to direct your lovemaking . . . and see how the sound of her own voice can be used to stimulate her.

Tell her that you have always secretly dreamed of having a woman make sexual demands on you. Say that you find it exciting to think of having a woman direct your lovemaking, then ask her to do just that, including each kiss and caress, each technique and position, even the pace of your copulation. Just the discussion of this should arouse her.

Though she may appear hesitant at first, she will become more and more enthusiastic as she begins to direct your lips and tongue to each sensitive area of her body, to command the thrusts of your hardened penis. She will be putting into words, perhaps for the first time, her sexual desires, thus violating the out-dated Puritan ethics upon which all of us were raised and indulging a "forbidden" pleasure; and she will be catering to the common desire to sexually dominate.

Don't be surprised to learn she has desires you never suspected, for this will surely bring them into the open. Satisfy them.

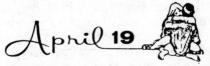

April 19

The navel is an erogenous zone that you may have neglected, so make up for that negligence tonight by showing her what your lips and tongue can do to this sensitive and potent area.

When she is partially stripped, or totally naked, circle her body with both arms and lower your lips to that delectable crease at the center of her stomach. Grip her buttocks with both hands, kneading them and encouraging the pumping of her hips, while you lick at her "belly button," swirling your tongue over it in swift circles, darting the tip of it into the soft crease; you should, in fact, use all the techniques of cunnilingus.

And cunnilingus, in fact, is what she will soon have you doing.

April 20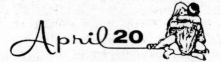

Those sex devices commonly known as "French ticklers" can be dangerous, according to many authorities, and are not recommended. But there is a way you can safely give her the same arousing effect.

You will need four very short, thick rubber bands. Place these around the shaft of your penis, after it is erect, and be sure they are not so tight as to cut off circulation or prevent ejaculation. Now cover the penis with an ordinary prophylactic . . . and give her the thrill of a lifetime!

The rubber bands create a ridge effect along the length of the penis, thus causing her clitoris to be moved several times with each thrust of your penis, and the prophylactic provides a smooth sheath that makes it all safe. It is perhaps the only way a condom can increase your sexual pleasure, so why not give it a try.

April 21

You know that the feel of her pubic hair and her moist vaginal flesh touching your face or body stimulates you as few other things can do, but do you know that your hardened penis and testicles can cause excitement for her in ways that have little to do with sexual intercourse? This is something of which you should be aware, and tonight you are going to try a little experiment that will show you how it works.

When the two of you are ready to make love, when she is naked and trembling with eagerness, turn on the bed and position yourself over her, one knee on each side of her head, your loins close to her face and your own face above her pubis, in the position that is most commonly used for simultaneous oral sex.

As you lower your head and begin to lick her waiting vagina, deliberately move your hips so that the tip of your penis moves against her face and lips. Delay her momentarily if she tries to take it in her mouth, and continue to move it against as much of her skin as possible. Let her both feel and see it.

Move it down to touch her breasts, if your position is such that you are able, and lower your hips to bring your testicles in contact with her face, while your tongue continues to dart in and out of her vagina. Prolong the contact.

If she has in the past been a somewhat reluctant fellatrice, or has never tried fellatio, this is one of the best ways to overcome her hesitancy; and if she is an experienced and eager oralist, the contact with your penis will excite and inspire her in a way that will make her efforts more mutually rewarding than ever before.

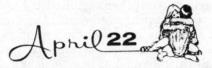

April **22**

Has she been reluctant, due to fear of pain or for other reasons, to try anal intercourse? Or does she truly love to feel your hard and throbbing penis moving deep in her anal canal? In either case, she will love the experience you are going to share with her tonight. She will readily agree if you explain that no penetration will be made unless she so desires—which she probably will.

Strip naked and lubricate her anus with vaseline or K-Y jelly, then stand behind her, your hands caressing her body, your lips brushing her shoulders or neck, and your hard erection pressing against her buttocks. Move one hand down to her vagina and slowly begin to masturbate her while your other hand toys with her breasts. As she begins to respond to these actions, carefully and gently place your penis in the cleft between her buttocks, so the swollen tip of it touches her anus. Make no attempt to penetrate her at his point.

Instead, continue to manipulate her clitoral mound until she begins to writhe with increased desire, a desire that will be all the greater because she feels your penis against her extremely sensitive anus. Soon, as she approaches her first orgasm, you are likely to feel her thrusting back to swallow your penis, for by now she will know something of the pleasure anal intercourse can give. In any case, her orgasm will be an excruciating one, as the nerves of the anus are part of a system extending to her clitoris.

But her orgasm will be nothing compared to your own.

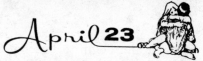

April 23

She wants to be told that her breasts are beautiful, tempting and desirable, and there is no better time than tonight to demonstrate to her just how exciting you think those firm mounds of flesh really are. And no better way than the following.

Tell her that her breasts were in your thoughts all day long, that you were unable to think of anything else, and that you want to have sex in a position that will allow you to fully enjoy the taste, sight, and feel of those wonderful spheres. Few women are going to resist such an approach.

Lie on your back and have her place one knee on each side of your body, so she is able to lower herself onto the shaft of your penis, and you, for your part, are able to admire and stroke her naked breasts. But this is merely the beginning.

As her hips begin to pump, her vagina lifting and falling over your erected penis, draw her upper body down and take one of her breasts into your mouth. Cover as much of the breast as possible, sucking steadily, and then lower your head, letting your lips slip over the naked flesh until only the nipple remains in your mouth. Then quickly refill your mouth with her flesh and repeat the process. Do this over and over, switching from breast to breast, and have your lips keep pace with the penis you are driving into her body.

The erotic combination of sensations you are providing will give her one of the most prolonged and intense series of orgasms she has ever known.

April 24

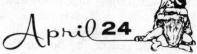

Display your artistic talents, and give her a chance to display hers, in a way that will soon have the two of you displaying talents that are totally sexual in nature.

Buy a set of fingerpaints, tell her that you intend to become a world-famous artist, and ask if you can practice your painting on her body. Offer your body as a "canvas" in exchange. Then, after getting her agreement, use your fingers to create the most erotic images imaginable on her naked skin, and enjoy the feel of her fingers applying paint to you.

There is a certain degree of exhibitionism in every female that will make getting her agreement much easier than you might suspect, and she is going to receive a great deal of sexual stimulation as she does her artistic work on your naked body. And don't worry about smudging the paint.

Washing it off can be as much fun as putting it on.

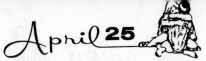

April 25

Here is an unusual method of cunnilingus that many women prefer above all others. It is best done while she sits in a comfortable chair, her legs flung wide, and you kneel between them with your face on the same level as her ready vagina.

Lift her legs and place them over your shoulders. Slip your hands, with the palms up, under her naked buttocks and lift until her vagina is against your face. Use your tongue to part the outer lips and lick her until her hips begin to move, then stiffen your tongue, extend it as deep as possible into her vagina, curl it up, and hold it there. Let the undulations of her hips move that sensitive flesh against your tongue. You can assist and encourage these undulations with your hands, if you so desire, but you are going to find she needs very little encouragement.

April 26

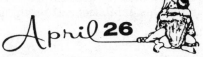

Visual erotica is sexually arousing to men and women alike, so what could be more exciting to her than a beautiful sex scene in which she is an active participant. The answer is nothing, and here is how you can make such a scene possible.

Place a mirror on the wall at the same level as the top of your bed, and very close beside it. It need not be a large mirror, but it should be placed so she will be able to glance at it and see the reflection of your penis as it enters her body, whether it be in her vagina, anus or mouth; or, if it is her preference, see the movement of her lower body as your tongue lavishes love on her vagina.

Let her decide which it is to be.

Imagine, if you can, the excitement she will feel as she lifts her eyes to catch a glimpse of her soft lips puckered around the tip of your penis, or as she watches the hypnotic thrusting of your manhood as it pierces her vagina. Stupendous!

April 27

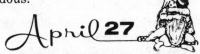

Moonlight means romance, and what could be more romantic than making love by moonlight? Nothing, so why not try it tonight?

If you have a patio or terrace that is hidden from the view of others, then you are especially fortunate and now is the time to put it to use; if not, a bed or sofa beside open windows so the soft light bathes your moving bodies while the cool night air flows around you will do almost as well.

You will soon see why moonlight is considered romantic.

April 28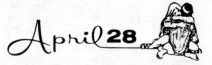

Any form of sex is proper as long as both partners enjoy it, yet all of us have certain inhibitions. The best way to help her overcome any inhibitions she may have is to discuss them calmly and objectively, and the best time to do this is after you have finished making love; not before, as this may lead her to believe you are trying to talk her into performing an act she does not like.

So wait until your lovemaking has relaxed her totally and then raise the subject. Ask her why she feels the way she does about oral sex, anal sex, or any other form of sex she considers taboo. Accept the reasons she gives you. Your questions will surely get her to thinking about the subject, and sometime in the very near future you may be happily surprised to discover that her inhibitions are a thing of the past.

April 29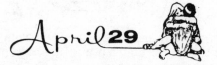

Few women will tolerate a man who allows himself to grow fat and sloppy, and obesity is something you should not tolerate in yourself. So take a long objective look at your physical condition and, if it is called for, begin a program of exercises designed to remove any excess fat. It requires only a few minutes a day to keep your body trim, and your efforts will be rewarded by the renewed interest she will show when it is time to make love.

April 30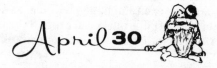

Give her a call from work, at an hour when she will still be in bed, and tell her you were unable to stop thinking of her and wanted to hear the sound of her voice. Let your own voice be filled with desire, and ask her to describe exactly what she is wearing. As she does, tell her that you wish you were there beside her, your hands caressing her naked flesh. Then ask her to pretend that you are, to touch various parts of her body while imagining the hands caressing her are yours, and try to get her to describe how it feels. She may or may not do this last, but of one thing you may be certain: She will be waiting, aroused and eager, when the day is over and you are able to go to her welcoming arms.

May 1

Sudden changes in temperature, especially when she expects them and knows you are using them to increase her sexual enjoyment, can cause delightful sensations that few other things can give. Here is a little trick that will cause her to experience an orgasm so powerful she will never forget it.

Mix two of your favorite drinks, but be sure the glasses contain plenty of cracked or crushed ice, and, far more important, be sure the erogenous zones of her body are exposed for what you are about to do.

As you use your hand to bestow intimate caresses on her body, take a bit of the ice into your mouth and hold it there, rolling it about with your tongue, while it melts. As the last of it turns to water, lean quickly down and take her nipple into your mouth. She will shiver at first, but as the coldness leaves your lips and tongue, the pleasure imparted by the sucking of your lips will become even greater than usual. Now smile at her as you repeat the melting process with the ice.

But this time lean down to let her feel your chilled lips and tongue lavishing love on her clitoris and vagina, the cold leaving as you lick, suck and kiss her, and see how she clings to the back of your neck as her hips begin to pump and her juices begin to flow.

May 2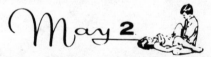

Are you sure that *your* inhibitions are not denying her the joy and satisfaction of a full and varied love-life? That may be the case if you have avoided certain types of sex because you felt she might be offended by the suggestion.

Tonight pick a form of sex—anal, oral, or whatever—that the two of you have never tried, and suggest to her that you see if it is enjoyable. Accept her refusal if she declines, but don't be surprised to discover that she is far less prudish than you thought.

Best estimates are that fully twenty-five percent of all females have tried anal sex at least once, a slightly smaller number enjoy it regularly, and you are out of touch with the times if you are unaware that a majority of women practice fellatio. Other statistics follow a similar pattern.

It may be that she has been waiting for you to take the lead, as many

women do, so why not take this opportunity to increase the range of your love-making?

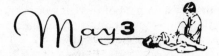

May 3

Do you know what caused her to experience her first orgasm? And do you know the form of her first sexual contact with a male? You should, because these experiences are held deep in her memory, and you can create a situation that will bring her subconscious into play and give her a delectable sexual experience.

It was masturbation that caused her first orgasm, unless she is a very unique woman indeed, and her first sexual contact with a male almost certainly occurred during a petting session, when she allowed a boy's hand to slip inside her panties while placing her own hand on his erected penis. Almost every female has had an experience similar to this.

Here is the way to use this knowledge.

Tonight, while sitting beside her on the sofa, take her in your arms and kiss her deeply. Let your tongue slip into her mouth. Then free her breasts and gently stroke them; lower your head and lick and suck her nipples, at the same time slipping one hand between her thighs.

Without slipping your finger into her vagina, which many women dislike, begin to masturbate her. Then, when you feel her juices start to flow, take her hand and place it over your erection, baring it if she does not do so herself. Continue massaging her clitoral mound with your fingers and, after a moment, you should feel her fist moving over your penis; if not, a touch on her wrist will give her the idea.

While most couples limit this mutual masturbation to foreplay, others find it a satisfying sex act when carried to climax as skilled fingers can cause an extremely intense orgasm. And many women really enjoy the act of masturbating a man, as there is an exciting sense of power to be had in the act of reducing a man to a mass of quivering flesh with only a few strokes of the hand. She may be one of these.

You'll never know till you give it a try.

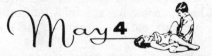

May 4

Lack of active participation on the part of the male is one of the most common objections among females who dislike performing fellatio. To remain totally passive while she licks, kisses, and sucks your hardened penis is the surest way of making her feel that she is subservient to your needs.

So tonight, after using words or body language to encourage her to fellate you, either briefly as a part of foreplay or as a complete sex act which she does while you perform cunnilingus, show her how exciting her fellation is by taking a more active role.

Let your hips roll gently so your thrusting penis moves to meet her bobbing lips, let your hands stroke her body, hair, and face, and let your words express the pleasure you feel as her lips or tongue touch each area of your naked loins. Let loving requests instruct the movements of her lips and let excitement be in your voice as you ask her to repeat an especially arousing caress. Words can be an exciting caress in their own right, and this is the time to use them.

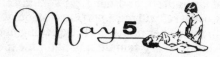

Have you fully explored the erotic potential of her buttocks? They are among her most potent erogenous zones, and tonight is as good a night as any to seek new ways in which they may be used to increase her sexual desire.

As you take her in your arms to kiss her, holding her so her pubis is pressed against your rising penis, let your hands slip under her buttocks, lifting her to her toes, and then press the firm but yielding mounds gently together, let your grip relax, and press them once again. Now stroke them lightly for a moment, press them together once again, and make a circular motion with your hands. They will soon begin to undulate with no help from you.

As her hips do begin slowly writhing, drop to your knees before her, your lips busy as you slip her panties down, exactly as you would do if you were going to perform cunnilingus. Which you are going to do—but later.

Cover her thighs with kisses as you use your hands to turn her so that you are facing her delectable buttocks—and then use your lips and tongue to show her just how delectable they are. Keep your arms around her body, your hands massaging her vagina, as you kiss and lick the sleek flesh of her rear, paying special attention to the cleft of her buttocks and the smooth, soft undercurves, for these areas are the most sensitive of all.

When at last you press your face to the delicious flesh of her vagina, you will find it wet and hot, ready to erupt into orgasm; and she will never forget the way you kissed her rear . . . and did it as an expression of love.

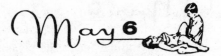

If Burt Reynolds can do it, then why not you?

Using a Polaroid camera with a timer, or with the help of a friend, take a nude photo of yourself. Buy a magazine that features nude male centerfolds, paste your photo over this, and give the magazine to her.

She will get a kick out of the idea, and you may even make jokes about it, but you can bet she will admire it when you are not around; for, though she may be reluctant to admit it, she is just as excited by nudity as you are.

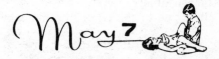

Buy her a bikini bathing suit, the tiniest, most revealing one you can find. Remind her that summer is just around the corner, tell her you bought it because you were excited by the thought of how it would temptingly reveal the lovely curves of her body, and ask her to model it for you.

Then, when she has it on, give her a lecherous grin, make a quick grab for her body, and admit that you really bought it so that there would be a lot less to remove.

Logic like that will surely convince her to remove it.

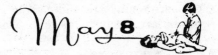

Simultaneous orgasm is something that most couples desire—and rightfully so—yet it can sometimes be difficult to achieve, especially if the female is extremely slow in reaching orgasm.

Here is a way your mind can help you bring about that perfectly timed orgasm. See how it works tonight.

When you are between her thighs making love and her tightly clinging vagina threatens to bring you to a premature climax, withdraw your penis slightly and, holding it there, try to visualize a scene that you would normally find nonsexual. You need only to do this briefly and the moment of orgasm will be delayed, but you can use it time and again, finally letting yourself go when she lifts her hips high and trembles in an orgasm to match your own.

What better way to use the power of mind over matter?

May 9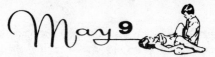

One of the best ways to introduce her to the pleasures anal sex can give is to encourage her to explore *your* anus and let her witness the pleasure this gives—and it will be pleasurable, for both the male and the female are subject to anal arousal.

So tonight, as you are making love or, if you are truly lucky, while she mouths your penis, guide her fingers to the cleft between your buttocks. Let your hips show your excitement as she tentatively explores your anal area, and soon she will be encouraged to insert the tip of her finger. The pleasure this gives has absolutely nothing to do with homosexuality, and this is one of the best ways to show her that anal contact really is pleasurable.

Soon she will allow you to show her in other ways.

May 10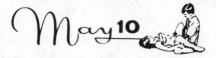

If you limit your cunnilingus to a brief performance prior to genital intercourse, then both of you are missing a great deal of the fun. Try interrupting your coitus and moving down to suck and lick her vagina into quivering ecstasy, then once again thrusting your penis in and out of her vagina, and you will probably find that your efforts are much more pleasing to her. The first thrusts of your penis will bring her clitoris to erection. The licking of your tongue will bring her to orgasm very quickly; and when you once again begin sliding your penis in and out of her vagina her orgasms are likely to be long, violent, and almost continuous.

And yours is going to be explosive.

May 11

Mild and harmless bondage is a form of sexual foreplay that many couples use to enhance their sexual activities, and there is really nothing wrong with it as long as it *is* kept mild and harmless. No real pain should be involved.

Suggest that you experiment with this exotic foreplay by having her tie you to the bed, your arms and legs spread, and allowing her to subject you to any sexual activity she desires during a specified time. She is more likely to accept this dominant role, as it seems to have the greater appeal to women, and you may be very surprised to see how uninhibited she becomes while you are at her mercy. She may also ask you to reverse the roles—in which case you should make every effort to show her how loving and kind you can be. But show her no sexual mercy!

Throw a few darts of love!

Here is a sexy little game that can turn a dull evening into a night of fun-filled love. You will need a set of darts to play.

Clip a photo of a nude man and a photo of a nude woman from any magazines in which you can find them. Paste each of these on individual boards, to be used as your targets. Write the number of points to be given for a hit on various parts of each photo, set a winning score, and decide on a penalty the loser must pay.

Then add another twist to the game.

Let her throw her darts at the female photo, you throw yours at the picture of the man, and agree that the other player must kiss the part of the anatomy penetrated by the dart. In this way, she is, when she scores, directing your kisses and you are able to do the same with hers.

Most women love playful sex games such as this, and you will likely find, after a few darts have been thrown and a few kisses given, that the game is becoming passionately serious.

Here is a female-dominant position for intercourse that she will love like no other, because it allows her such splendid freedom of movement in the pelvic area, thus making it possible for her to more fully enjoy your lovemaking. You may have to explain the position to her.

You lie on your back with your legs close together, and she moves over you with her knees spread. Placing her hands above your shoulders to partially support her weight, she now moves one foot toward yours, so that her leg is extended beside yours and her vagina is ready to settle over your erection. She will now be leaning far forward, with one leg bent at the knee, the other straight, and she will begin to whisper expressions of pleasure as her rolling hips slip her vagina up and down the shaft of your penis. She is in a very comfortable position, awkward though it may sound, so your hands are left free to caress her back, breasts and buttocks. And to hold her tight when she reaches orgasm.

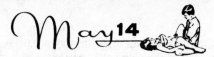

May 14

Tonight let her make advances to you. Such a happening is easy to bring about if you go about it in the proper way . . . and this is a way that is almost sure to work.

Shower, shave, apply a bit of cologne, and then, wearing no other clothes, slip into a robe. Belt it around your waist and go out to join her. As you talk to her, say nothing about sex, but let your tone of voice be soft and intimate.

She will be fully aware of your bare legs, of the nakedness beneath that robe, and soon you will find her beside you; when that occurs, take her in your arms, kiss her, but make no further move until you feel her hand slipping beneath the robe to explore your nakedness. Which will happen before you know it.

May 15

Here is one of the very few positions which allows the two of you to engage in anal intercourse while she faces you, and she will find it highly enjoyable because it allows you to suck and fondle her breasts while sliding your hardened penis through the tight canal of her anus.

Don't let the night go by without giving it a try!

After the two of you have removed your clothing and her anus has been lubricated with a suitable lubricant such as vaseline or K-Y jelly, sit down on a narrow chair with your legs close together and have her spread her feet far apart as she stands facing you. Now place your hands on the backs of her thighs and slowly draw her closer, keeping her legs outside your own.

Slip your hands lower, to her buttocks, and spread them wide as you ease her down onto your stiffened penis—and ease her down slowly, so the penetration will be more enjoyable for her. And as she begins to move up and down on your impaling erection, assisted by your hands under her rear, make the entire act more thrilling for her by using all your skills as you suck and lick her stiffened nipples.

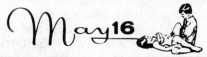

May 16

Brush her hair for her!

This may sound foolish to you, but there is something about having the hair brushed by another person that causes most women to feel pampered—and you really should pamper her now and then.

With this small but highly expressive show of affection, you can convince her of your love in a way that words could never do.

And it is safe to say she will express her own love in return—but not by brushing your hair!

Let her have a night out with the girls.

Like most men you probably spend a night out now and then (though you may not waste it on "the boys"), so why should she not have a free night on occasion? Suggest that she go out on the town.

It is the best way to show your trust, and the best way to win her fidelity. She will be pleased by your thoughtfulness, happy because of your faith, and will reward you for both at a later time.

Use her electric hair-dryer to arouse her—then enjoy the results.

It should be the hand-held type that has a blower, and you should be careful to see that neither of you are standing in water when it is used. Have it ready when she steps out of the shower or tub.

Ask her to let you dry her body, then, after she agrees, use the warm flow of air from the dryer to remove the moisture from her skin, letting it linger long and lovingly on her thighs, breasts, buttocks and, especially, on her moistened pubes.

And don't hesitate if she asks to do the same to you.

The best lover is one who has a keenly developed tactile sense, for it is this sense, perhaps more than any other, that causes your sexual reactions. Here is an exercise designed to hone to a fine edge your sense of touch. Try it today and repeat it often.

Gather a number of household items, each having a different texture, such as a drinking glass, a satin pillow, a fur piece, an item or two of her underclothes. Strip naked, close your eyes, and touch each of the items to various parts of your body. Try hard to remember the feel of each, and take the exercise seriously. It will help you develop an aura of sensuality.

May 20

Here is a simple technique that will greatly increase her enjoyment of intercourse when using the ordinary man-above or, as it is often called, "missionary" position. Why not learn how it works tonight, so you can use it to give her more pleasure in the future?

As you lie above her and between her parted thighs, and her hips begin to lift and roll in response to your thrusting penis, try thrusting your penis in as far as it will go, holding it there with all your strength, so the bony plate at the top of your groin is tight against the soft mound above hers; then, pressing hard, move your hips from side to side repeatedly. This side-to-side motion may be enough to cause her to experience orgasm the first time it is used, or you may want to relax the pressure, let her feel a few more strokes of your penis, and try it again.

In either case she will squeal with delight as you do it.

May 21

Take her out for a night of dining and dancing, or for any other activity you think she will enjoy. And then, when the evening is over, instead of returning home, take her to the motel where you have reserved a room. Vigor is added to your lovemaking by a change of place, as well as by a change of pace, and that vigor will be worth every dime you pay for the room.

May 22

Rear-entry positions are among the favorites of most female because of the greater contact between the penis and the clitoris, and the pleasure becomes even greater when the position used is one she finds comfortable.

The position to which you are going to introduce her tonight is one she will love, because it offers both comfort and the ease of movement that allows her to swivel her pelvis back to meet your driving penis with her vagina.

Have her kneel on an armchair, when she is naked and ready for love, with her knees apart and near the outer edge of the cushion, her forearms resting on the back of the chair. She can then, if she wishes, rest her face against her arms as you step close behind her and, with your hands caressing her nudity, insert the hard shaft of your penis from the rear. Not only is this an excellent position but it adds a little spice to the act by taking it out of the bedroom for a change.

You can more easily direct your lovemaking into the proper channels if you know the images that fill her mind as she makes love, so try to get her to disclose her sex fantasies. All women have them, as do men, and they are a key to understanding her hidden desires.

Get her in the mood to disclose these fantasies by describing one or two of your own. You know what they are. Tell her you are a little ashamed of having them and are afraid they might not be normal. She will probably assure you that they are—and prove it by describing a few of her own. Remember them and act on them.

Do you believe that body contact, pure and simple, without sexual penetration and without cunnilingus, can cause a woman to experience orgasm? It can, and you had better believe it. Just listen to the following facts.

A recent survey that was equal in size and scope to the Kinsey survey of years past (it was sponsored by the Playboy Foundation) found that, contrary to what most people believe, less than fifty percent of the lesbians interviewed have engaged in cunnilingus or used an artificial sex organ—yet most have experienced orgasm brought on by body contact! See if you can match that!

There are psychological factors involved here, and you may not be able to bring her to orgasm merely by pressing your naked body to hers while your tongue fills her mouth and your hands caress her breasts and buttocks, but why not give it a try? Both of you will enjoy the effort, at the very least.

Here is a method of sexual intercourse that is strictly for fun, though the terrific sensations it provides, the two of you will discover, are nothing to laugh about.

Sit on the edge of the bed with your feet on the floor while she stands facing you, naked. Lock your arms around her, half-rising to your feet, and let her throw her legs around your waist. As you insert your penis, once again resume your sitting position, so her legs are extended onto the bed behind your back. Grasp her arms near the shoulders and ask her to lean slowly back as far as she can. Let her arms slip through your hands until you are grasping her wrists, then pull her back up until her breasts are against your chest. Fabulous!

Ask her to go for a drive, and take her out to a lonely hill where you can sit close together and watch the sunset. Such moments are what most women long for in a relationship, and you will soon find her in a very romantic mood. Be just as intimate as the loneliness of the spot permits, and remember—sunsets are always followed by darkness, which will allow even more intimacy.

Stop by a bookstore and buy a book containing erotic pictures, selecting one that offers as much variety as possible. Then leave it where she will be sure to find it.

Visual displays of fellatio, cunnilingus, sexual intercourse, anal intercourse, and group sex are just as exciting to her as they are to you, though she may not like to discuss it, and you can bet this excitement will show in her lovemaking later tonight.

Let her help you make your cunnilingus so effective she will literally crave the feel of your tongue against her clitoris from this night forward. Her greater participation makes it work.

As you kneel with your head between her thighs, and after a few strokes of your tongue have aroused her desire, lift your face slightly and, in a husky whisper, ask her which parts of her loins she most likes you to touch. Ask her to touch them with the tip of a finger so you will know, and flick the tip of your tongue across her flesh and her finger as she does. Then ask her to hold her clitoris with her fingers so you may lick it, and let arousing strokes of your tongue convince her she should. You will soon have her writhing wildly before your face, and her own fingers will have helped you do it.

Spend a few minutes telling her just how pleased you were by a certain night of lovemaking the two of you shared—and see how eager she becomes to relive that night.

Hold her in your arms and describe in vivid, breathless detail how the image of that night lingers in your memory. Recall how she looked as she fellated you, or twisted with excitement as you drove your penis at her hot, wet vagina. Describe how it felt, and remind her of the words you exchanged. Tell her you think of it constantly.

This type of sex talk is both flattering and arousing to most females, and soon she will be eager to do more than just talk about it.

Most bathrooms have both a tub and a shower, and here is a way you can use that combination to fill her body with the most exquisite sensations she has ever known.

Run two or three inches of water in the tub and have her lie naked in it. Adjust the shower nozzle so it gives off a narrow spray that is about body temperature, and direct this stream at the rise of her pubis. Sit on the edge of the tub and lean down to kiss, suck, and fondle her breasts, to stroke her body and thrust your tongue in her mouth, as the heavy stream of water brings her closer and closer to orgasm. She will place herself so it hits the most sensitive areas.

This is a method of masturbation used by many females, and it causes a terrific orgasm. With you there to help, the orgasm will be that much better.

The U.S. Copyright Law was enacted on this date in 1970, so why not celebrate by breaking—or at least bending—it. Copy a love poem, give it to her, and give her a kiss along with it, as you tell her it is your own creation.

You may have trouble writing much more than your own name, and she may darned well know it and make you admit where you got the poem, but she will still appreciate the thought.

June 1

Warm weather is here and it is time for a little summer fun!

Ask her to join you for a little sunbathing, and do it in the most private spot available. Have a bottle of tanning lotion on hand, and let her relax so you gently apply it to her body, and don't hesitate to mention that she will get a more even tan if she loosens and lowers her bikini.

Privacy permitting, she may choose to remove it altogether.

June 2

We all love receiving an unexpected gift now and then, so why not surprise her with the most erotic gift you could possibly give? Stop by a store which sells sex articles (most adult bookstores do) and ask for a set of "Wa-Wah Balls," or "Oriental Golden Balls." They were recommended by no less an authority than Dr. David Reuben, as the most effective device a female might use for autostimulation.

They are inserted into the vagina and held there by a Tampax, and with each move she makes, each step she takes, they click together, continually shifting in a way that will bring her to orgasm as she goes about her normal chores around the house.

Instructions are included, and though she may pretend not to be interested, female curiosity will soon get the better of her. You will know this has happened when you return home to find her so aroused that she seems ready to give off sparks of sexual energy.

That is when both of you begin to enjoy the gift.

June 3

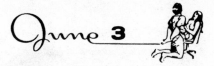

Here is a position that allows only limited movement of the penis, but is highly enjoyable nonetheless. Perhaps the reason it is so exciting is because it forces her to work for all she gets. Try it.

Lie on your side behind her, your arms around her body and your hands stroking her breasts, as you begin making love. When your penis is deep inside her and she begins to writhe, hold her tight and roll onto your back, so she is also on her back above you. Doing this may cause your penis to slip free, but she will quickly replace it.

You will find that you are able to keep little more than the tip of your penis in her from this position, and both your and her movements are limited, but your hard flesh that *is* inside her will be pressed against her clitoris as never before, and the hand she automatically presses to her loins to hold you there will further increase her excitement.

So who needs a lot of movement?

June 4

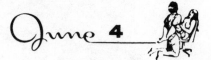

Here is a simple technique of cunnilingus that will cause her to feel incredible excitement from the first to the last touch of your tongue. Give it a conscientious try tonight.

Have her lie on her back while you assume a prone position between her parted thighs, so you are facing her vagina. Now place one hand over her mons, that soft rise of flesh above her vagina, and turning your wrist, use your thumb and forefinger to gently press her labia, the outer lips of her vagina, together, so they form a ridge of pink flesh. Now run the tip of your tongue up and down this ridge.

Lick her faster and faster, not letting your tongue part the lips as you normally would, until you feel her straining hard to draw your face against her flesh. Then begin to explore her inner vagina, and you will find the clitoris stiff between your lips, ready to erupt in orgasm.

June 5

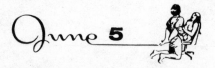

Change the pace of your lovemaking, if only for this single night. To do so now and then creates a powerful effect.

All men tend to follow a set pace during copulation, especially if they have been with the same woman for any length of time, and nothing takes the edge off her excitement faster than repetition.

So if your normal routine is to make love to her with hard, fast thrusts of your penis, try taking the opposite tack tonight; let your loving be slow and leisurely. If slow, gliding thrusts are your normal technique, try changing to hammering strokes that cause skin to slap against skin.

It will make a new woman out of her!

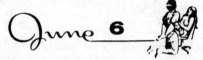

June 6

Give her a tongue bath!

Many consider this the ultimate erotic experience, and it may be just that. It will surely arouse her as few other acts can do.

Have her lie naked on the bed while your tongue flickers over her throat, breasts, stomach, and pubes, continuing down over her thighs, ankles, and feet. Linger long and lovingly over her buttocks and anus before letting your tongue caress her spine and back; and then finally, press your face to the delectable flesh of her vagina and let your tongue give a "bath" to the inner parts of her body.

You will probably find these parts hot and wet with the sweet juices of orgasm.

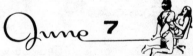

June 7

Here is an exercise in sensuality that is designed to strengthen your tongue so you can put it to more effective use when you are with her. Try the exercise today and practice it regularly.

Use a small glass of the type in which whiskey is served. Hold it to your lips, as if preparing to drink from it, but have your lips parted wide. Extend your tongue as far as you can, so it goes deep into the glass, and taking away your hand, try to support the weight of the glass with your tongue. Try to do this longer with each attempt, and when it becomes easy, substitute a heavier glass.

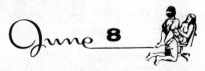

June 8

Her spinal column is an erogenous zone that you may have overlooked, so why not concentrate, tonight, on learning ways in which it may be used to arouse her and increase her sexual pleasure?

As you hold her in your arms to kiss her, run your hand up and down her back, pausing to massage the small of her back, and try tapping your fingers up and down her spine, moving them as you would do if playing a flute. And when she is naked, see how she shivers with delight as you do the same with your tongue. She will be shivering in anticipation of what is to come.

June 9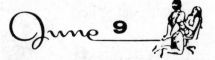

Here is a position that offers tremendous delights! Try it!

When the two of you are excited, naked, and ready to make love, have her sit in a comfortable armchair. You kneel between her legs (perhaps using your tongue to increase her excitement), with your legs together and your buttocks resting on your heels. Now slip your hands around her waist and help her to *slide* slowly off the chair and onto your erection. With her elbows now resting on the cushion of the chair, she will find it easy to raise and lower herself over the hard shaft of your penis; and with your hands under her buttocks, when they are not fondling her breasts, you will find it a pleasure to assist her.

June 10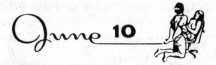

Let her walk into the bedroom and find you wearing nothing but a smile!

After telling her you are tired and have had a rough day, add that you feel like a nap. Go into the bedroom, remove all your clothing, and lie naked across the bed. Now let your mind create erotic images, stimulating an erection. Maintain that erection until she opens the door to look in on you.

And maintain the smile as you reach for her and tell her you are never *that* tired.

June 11

The position you assume while she performs fellatio can greatly affect her attitude toward this act. It can help to make her an eager fellatrice—or it can increase her reluctance. So give a little consideration to the psychological factors that are involved here.

Many women actually like to be dominated, and this desire is catered to if she kneels before you while kissing and sucking your penis, or if she takes a passive stance while you drive it in and out of her mouth. Verbally directing her fellation also gives a suggestion of dominance.

Other women strongly resent any hint of dominance by the male, and will find the act more enjoyable if you assume a passive posture. This type woman will sometimes have a desire to dominate *you*, though she may be unaware of it, and that desire is fulfilled as she leans down over you and sees how, with her lips and tongue, she has reduced your hardness to quivering jelly.

Take these things into consideration, tonight, as you seek new ways to make oral sex more enjoyable for her. And don't forget to reciprocate.

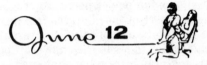

Ask her to wear a blindfold while you make love to her!

For her to lie naked on the bed, not knowing where to expect the next touch of your lips, hands or erected penis, not knowing if it will come on her naked breasts, thighs, buttocks or vagina, is one of the most exciting things a woman can experience. And as the blindfold encourages her to fantasize freely while your tongue or penis moves in and out of her vagina, her orgasms, when they come, will be an experience she will long remember.

Explain to her how this will increase the erotic impact of your lovemaking, get her agreement, and be imaginative while you prolong her pleasure with every device of love you know. Both of you will agree, after tonight, that true love is truly blind.

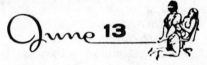

Fantasy plays an important role in the sex life of almost every person, and you should know how to use her fantasies to make the reality of sex more exciting. Try this technique that plays upon one of the most common female fantasies. It may just double her pleasure.

Do not mention the fantasy, but let her know that you have an idea in mind which you are sure she will enjoy, and get her agreement. Have one of those penis-shaped, battery-operated vibrators (hers, or one from a drugstore) on hand. Make her wonder how you intend using it.

Encourage her into a side-by-side position for simultaneous fellatio and cunnilingus and lick and kiss her until she responds by fastening her lips to your hardened penis. Then, gently and without words, insert the humming vibrator into her vagina and slide it in and out while she fellates you—and you wait until you see how excitedly she does so.

You see, it is extremely *common* for a woman to imagine that she is having sex with two or more men at the same time, and you have just made that fantasy a near-reality for her. And wait till you see and feel what it does for you!

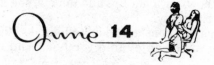

$\mathcal{J}$une 14

Make a Liberated Woman out of her!

Bralessness was the mark of the liberated female in the early days of the movement, so wait until an opportunity presents itself, then hide all her bras. Do this while she is in the shower, if possible, so she will have none to wear. Jokingly inform her that she has been "liberated," and see if you can talk her into going out to dinner with no bra beneath her dress.

If she agrees—and she may surprise you by doing so—make flattering comments about her breasts throughout the evening. And even if she disagrees, think of all the fun you will have as she tries to coax you into telling where you hid the bras.

$\mathcal{J}$une 15

You know how exciting it is to you to feel the flimsy nylon of her panties, bra, and hose caressing your naked skin, but are you aware that those same garments can be stimulating to *her?* Tonight is the night to discover just how stimulating they can be.

Tonight, when her bra straps have been loosened, instead of hastily removing the bra as you might normally do, let your hands linger over the delectable globes until her nipples stiffen beneath the thin nylon; try sucking her nipples while the bra lies loosely over them. Then move your lips down to the nylon covering her vagina.

Lick and suck this a moment before lowering the panties, and, as you tug those down her thighs, use your fingertips to move the nylon enticingly over her bare skin. If she is wearing hosiery, loosen it and be slow, ever so slow, as you teasingly peel it off her legs.

Then take her in your arms and soothe her.

June 16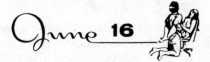

Be a little bit vulgar with her! That's right, use "those words."

As you hold her in your arms, kissing and touching her in preparation for the moment of love, use explicit slang of the most vulgar nature as you refer to the various parts of her body and of your own, and be naughtily explicit as you describe what you hope to do to her, or have her do to you.

As you begin making love, continue to describe, in the language of the streets, the sensations you feel, making constant reference to the parts of her body giving you these pleasures.

Sex talk of this type is highly exciting to a great number of females and is, in fact, practiced by an even greater number; so don't be surprised if, as she approaches orgasm, she outdoes you by suddenly chanting a stream of words that are even beyond your vocabulary.

Women know these words, too.

June 17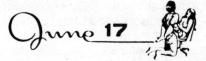

Make her Queen for a Day!

Tell her you were thinking of that old radio program, realized that no woman was more deserving of royal treatment than she, and you have decided to make her your queen for this day . . . with a single hitch.

You will be her sexual servant, performing any sexual service she may desire, as frequently as she may desire, with your own pleasure becoming secondary to hers. She chooses the act and position.

Be sure to treat her royally!

June 18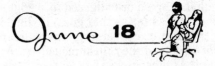

Have you been hesitant to perform cunnilingus on her because you feel that it might somehow lower her opinion of you? Odd as this question may sound to those men who regularly lick and lap the vagina of the females in their lives and thus know cunnilingus to be one of the most exciting things a man can do to a woman, there are those who do not quite know how to make the first oral approach to a woman.

Try approaching her like this.

As she lies naked and waiting, let your lips begin to wander over her breasts, stomach, and thighs, finally coming to rest over the hairy triangle of her pubis. Kiss this tenderly, as if it were an object of worship, and then do the same to the pink flesh of her outer vaginal lips. Her natural response will be to grasp you in a way that presses your mouth to her, and this response, more than anything else, clearly demonstrates how natural the act of cunnilingus is; the response is also the signal for you to let your tongue run wild in her vagina.

Even if you regularly perform cunnilingus on her, try bestowing those tender kisses upon her outer vagina tonight, for it is a clear demonstration of the love you feel for it as a part of her.

June 19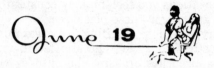

Sex is always good (or, at least, never really bad), but there are ways in which it can be made absolutely wonderful. Here is one.

Place a rubber mat in the bathtub, to spare your knees, and fill the tub halfway with warm water. Add a little bubble bath and have her lie down in it. Then join her.

With the warm water giving a pleasurable buoyancy to her breasts as you fondle them, and her hips and thighs made warmer and lighter by the same water, her body surrounded by warmth as your even warmer penis fills her inner vagina, she will thrill to this luxurious way of making love. And so will you.

June 20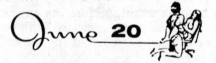

No woman should be forced or badgered into engaging in anal intercourse (or any other act, as far as that goes) if she does not enjoy it or has no desire to try it; but, conversely, any woman who does enjoy analism should not be denied the fullest pleasure the act can give. Here is one way to give that pleasure.

While your penis moves in her rear, reach around her body and use one hand to manipulate her clitoris and the other to caress her nipples; for even though sexual pleasure is derived from anal penetration, few women will reach orgasm solely because of this stimuli and you must manually accomplish this.

When you reach your own climax, do not withdraw your penis, but keep it there while you continue to masturbate her, for the warmth of your semen flooding her anus and the subsequent fading of your erection can cause the most delightful sensations of all; these and the manipulations of your fingers will soon have her trembling with orgasm.

Don't deny her these pleasures tonight.

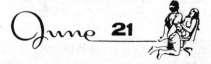

June 21

Ask her to join you in a little test that will help the two of you become a more loving couple. She wants that as much as you.

Sit down together and make a list of every sex act you can think of, including those you think of as deviant behavior. Leave nothing off the list, not even the most bizarre acts. Make two copies of this list, and each of you take one.

Now secretly, but honestly, put a check mark beside those acts which, if given the chance and assured of no bad repercussion, you would agree to try; draw a line through those in which you would not engage under any circumstances. Have her do the same.

Now compare lists to see who is the most inhibited. If you have answered honestly, the answers are going to prove surprising to both of you; and, in any case, the one who gave the most negative answers is going to be encouraged to take a close look at his or her attitudes.

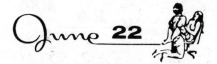

June 22

Technique is an important part of cunnilingus, it goes without saying, but so is the position you use while licking and sucking her to orgasm. Here is a terrific position, one that places you in a submissive posture and gives her the added pleasure of knowing you will almost literally get down on your knees and beg for a taste of the delectable flesh which lies between her thighs. Most women love to believe that, and you should strengthen that belief—tonight!

While she sits in a comfortable armchair, kneel on the floor at her feet and let your desire show in your eyes as, caressing her thighs, you tug down her panties to reveal the tasty morsel beneath.

Now lift her legs and drape them over your shoulders, and then, slipping your hands under her buttocks, lift her rear from the chair. As you bend lower and cover her vagina with your lips, your tongue darting in, you will feel her hands on your neck and hear her whispering heated words of encouragement.

That is what you get when you treat her like the dish she is.

June 23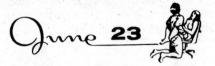

Every movement you make during intercourse, each touch, kiss and caress, is stamped someplace on her memory. In most cases, it is a part of her subconscious and never recalled; but in other, more erotic, instances, it may remain vivid in her mind and become a moment upon which she may fantasize while the two of you are making love.

Give her such a moment tonight.

Make love to her using the male-dominant position, and withhold your climax till after she has reached orgasm. Then, when you do feel yourself preparing to ejaculate, suddenly and without a word, free your penis and lift yourself up, so she sees the spewing semen as it spatters hotly against her pubis, stomach, or, perhaps, even her breasts.

No need to explain it to her, but the sight of the ejaculating penis is very, very exciting to many woman, as is the vision of having hot seminal fluid spraying the naked body.

She will remember it . . . pleasantly!

June 24

Sit down and plan your budget so that you will be able to take a day off work—and plan on spending that day making love.

Your working hours can be lonely and boring for her, and you will find that her sexual desires—and your own—are much more easily aroused during those times when you would not normally be together. There is no need to worry about getting to sleep on time; she needs not worry about getting your dinner or doing other chores; there is time to make love, rest, and regain your energy, then make love again.

It will be more than worth any wages you may lose.

June 25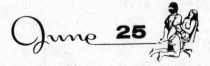

Surprise her with a kiss when she least expects it—and make it more surprising by kissing her *where* she least expects it!

Wait until she passes you as you sit on the sofa or in a chair and, suddenly reaching out to throw your arms around her thighs, draw her close and plant a long, nuzzling kiss on the sloping vee that leads to her vagina. At the next opportunity catch her again and press your lips to the curves of her buttocks. Catch her as often as you can.

Though she is probably going to be fully clothed as you do this, you can bet she will be aware of what you are suggesting with those kisses, and will be stirred by them.

So stirred you will have to repeat them when she is nude.

June 26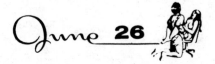

Anilingus, the use of the tongue on the anus, is so stimulating that it alone causes many women (or men, while we're on the subject) to experience orgasm. But why not use it as a part of your foreplay and make her orgasms during coitus more intense than ever before?

Kneeling behind her and spreading her naked buttocks with your hands, press your lips to the cleft and touch her anus teasingly with the tip of your tongue. Move it in swift circles, flick it up and down, then stiffen it and try to thrust it into the anus. This will be difficult at first, but as she relaxes, her resistance will lessen and your tongue will feel literally drawn into the tight circle of flesh.

You should always remember that her anus is a self-cleaning apparatus, free of fecal matter except immediately after defecation, and you should approach it as you would any other part of her body.

So why not approach it tonight?

June 27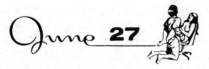

Buy yourself a little gift that she will enjoy as well. The two of you are going to be out in the sun very often this summer, so why not be wearing a brief, brief bikini that will draw her eyes to your crotch and constantly remind her of the pleasure-giving flesh hidden beneath the skimpy bit of cloth?

You may not be built like Adonis, but your body is attractive to her. This is an easy and natural way to display it, and you should use it at every opportunity.

June 28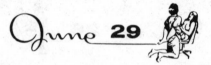

Stop by a well-stocked record shop and take a careful look at the albums available. Many erotic recordings are now sold, some of them including the sounds of couples making love. These can be very, very arousing; but if these are not to be had, select some good "mood" music, pieces with a heady, erotic beat, and play them tonight while you are with her.

Learn what is meant by the phrase, "Music to make love by."

June 29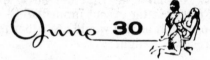

You know of course that the touch of her silk and nylon undergarments is delicious to you, but have you considered the many ways in which various materials can be exciting to her? Here is one.

When she steps out of the shower have two towels on hand. One should be a regular bath towel, and you use this to dry her. The other should be a large beach towel, made of terry cloth, big enough to cover most of her body, and it will be more exciting to her if it is warm from the dryer. Drape this over her body, slipping your arms around her to hold it there, as you kiss her deeply. It will be caressing each inch of her naked skin as you do.

June 30

Take her for a moonlight swim.

The pools and beaches are less crowded at night, giving you more opportunities to engage in intimate horseplay, and the moonlight on the water is bound to stir her romantic instincts. Be sure to take along a blanket big enough to cover the two of you and protect you from the chilly night air—and from the prying eyes of other swimmers.

July 1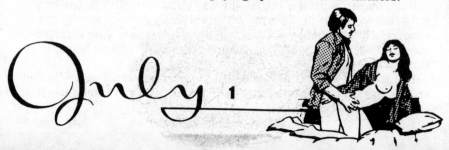

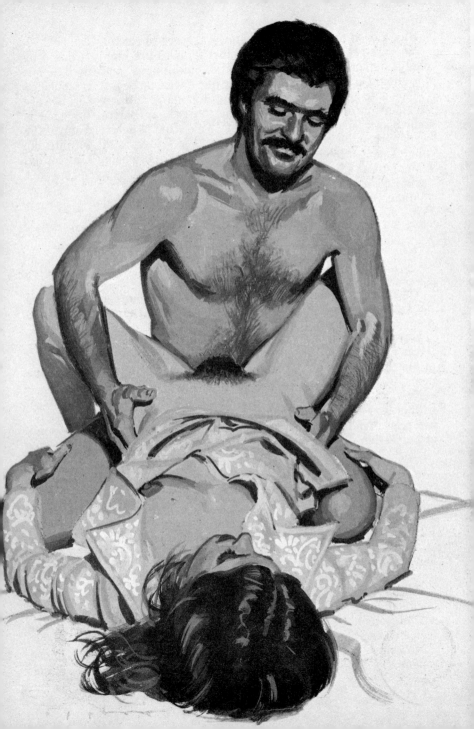

Buy a *good* erotic novel and encourage her to read it.

You are probably aware that most females are highly aroused by photos depicting intercourse, fellatio, cunnilingus, and the like, but you should know that reading about these acts can be just as arousing.

This is so because any good writer (and many authors of erotica are excellent ones, no matter what the censors say) strives for what is known as a "suspension of disbelief." This effect is achieved only if the reader, through words that play upon the senses, is drawn into the story, seeing it in vivid images, perhaps even experiencing it, mentally, along with the fictional characters. Thus, if the book is a good one, her sexual desires are going to be stirred in many ways.

Make yourself available when she puts the book aside.

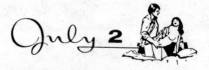

Try this way of changing the angle with which your penis penetrates her vagina, and see if it doesn't make a delightful change in her enjoyment of intercourse. It usually does.

Have her lie naked on her back, her legs parted, while you kneel between her thighs with your body erect. Slip your hands under the backs of her upper legs and lift them around your waist as you insert your penis, hooking your elbows behind her knees.

Now, as you slowly begin pumping your hips, continue to gradually lift her legs higher, thus slowly changing the angle of penetration. Her low cries of delight will let you know when you have reached the point of perfection. Let perfection be your goal as you continue.

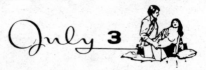

Here is a method of cunnilingus that allows her to guide and use your stiffened tongue in the way that is most satisfying to her, and you can bet she will continue to use it till she begins thrashing wildly with orgasm. So why not let her "use" you tonight?

Place a couple of pillows on the bed and lie on your back with your head supported and lifted by them. Have her place one knee on each side of your head, keeping her body erect and her back toward your feet, her vagina poised directly over your face.

Now put your hands on her buttocks and thrust out your stiffened tongue as you lift your face to the hair-surrounded flesh of her vagina.

Thrust your tongue between the dewy outer lips and hold it there as firm and unyielding as you can keep it, while your hands on her buttocks encourage her to swing her hips back and forth. She will soon get the idea, and her pelvis will begin to pump and turn, moving her body so that your tongue is drawn repeatedly over the vaginal parts that are most in need of your touch.

And she knows even more about those than you.

July 4

Independence Day

The traditional way to celebrate this day is to go to a park or civic picnic and watch the display of fireworks, but why not make your own celebration more interesting? It will also be a lot more fun.

Invite her to go with you to watch the fireworks, then head for a dark country lane. Hold her close and make small talk until she asks when the fireworks start, then kiss her and put one hand over her breast, the other slipping beneath her skirt, and tell her you planned to create fireworks of your own.

Then let the fireworks begin!

July 5

There should be no stigma attached to fellatio, for it is as natural as breathing, yet many women who perform this act of love continue to suffer feelings of guilt caused by misunderstanding and false ethics upon which they may have been raised; and other women, perhaps even more unfortunate, continue to deprive themselves of the pleasures an uninhibited sex life can give.

Tonight begin to free her from the chains of the past.

Go to the library and pick up a copy of the Kinsey Report, or any other major work of this type, plus one or two books on the psychology of sex. The statistics given in these books may vary slightly, as may the approach, but upon one thing they all agree: No act is perverted if it is a mutually enjoyable act performed by two people as a part of love.

Now take a look at a few of the statistics.

You will quickly see that oral love is, was, and always will be a natural part of the relationship between a man and a woman. It is regularly enjoyed by millions of people, and there is no reason the woman in your life should deny herself this pleasure, or feel anything but joy when she indulges.

Letting her clearly see that her friends and neighbors almost certainly partake of fellatio is one of the best ways to help the girl who has doubts overcome them; and it is not a matter of nagging, in this case; it is a matter of giving her information she should have.

And what if she regularly fellates you? Well, can you think of a better way to bring up the subject?

July 6

Just as you love to stroke her breasts and buttocks while making love, she, too, can derive added pleasure by holding tight to certain parts of your body; but she may be too shy to do this, or may be unaware of the added pleasure it can give.

So tonight give her a little encouragement.

Once or twice during the foreplay, while you stroke or suck her naked breasts, take her hand and guide it to your testicles or erected penis, and see how this increases her excitement. Then, as you prepare to make love, encourage her to take a kneeling position with her legs parted, so you can enter her vagina from the rear. When your penis is deep inside her and moving, when her buttocks writhe before you, take one of her hands and guide it back between her thighs until her fingers touch the sac of your testicles.

Soon you will feel her fingers stroking and flexing, tightening in reaction to each hard plunge of your penis, and never again will you have to guide her hand, for you have just shown her a small device that gives added pleasure to both of you.

July 7

Try this position for anal intercourse. It is a frontal position that allows you to admire the beauty of her body, and her, yours, while anal penetration is made. She may find it more comfortable if a soft pillow is placed under her buttocks or the small of her back before you begin.

After thoroughly lubricating her anus with vaseline or K-Y jelly, have her lie on her back with her legs parted. Kneel between her thighs, keeping your body erect, and lift her buttocks very high, so her weight is thrown on her upper back and her legs, resting against your shoulders, are pointed almost straight up. She will find it easy to reach down with both hands and spread her buttocks wide as you insert your penis, and the anal experience which follows will be all the more enjoyable for both of you because of your facing position.

Change the sheets on the bed for her—and change those sheets into a real sensory treat.

Stop by a department store and buy a set of satin sheets. You will be able to choose from a wide variety of colors that add to the erotic atmosphere of the bedroom—red, midnight black, or emerald, for instance—and you will find they are relatively inexpensive.

Say nothing to her and put them on the bed, so that later she will be in for a delectable surprise as she awakens to the sleek luxury they surround her with while you make love.

You will agree they are a real bargain, at almost any price.

She wants to be an exciting lover, as any female does, but she may be one of those few women who really dislike having a hard penis inside her mouth, or, a little more probably, she may dislike fellatio because of the tendency to gag on the ejaculated semen.

So tonight, as you perform cunnilingus on her, show her how she can achieve the same results without actually taking the shaft of your penis into her mouth. The thrills she gives to you in this manner will impart themselves to her, thus increasing the pleasure she receives from your darting, lapping tongue.

Ask her to try licking the underside of your penis, which is the area that causes most of your excitement, and explain to her that the same result can be had by swirling her tongue over the very tip of your penis, or flicking this tip lightly. Then quit talking and return your tongue to its proper place between her thighs.

If oral sex is a relatively new experience for her, she will be a little more eager to try it in these ways; and even if she is a very experienced fellatrice, she may be unaware of these simple techniques.

But in either case you should remember to keep your own lips and tongue busy, for you should never expect to receive more than you are willing to give.

$\mathcal{July}$ 10

The inner thighs are one of her more important erogenous zones, and tonight is the night to give them a little special attention and learn just how important they can be to your lovemaking.

When first you take her in your arms to kiss her, your tongue going deep in her mouth, try lifting your knee and forcing your own leg between her thighs, moving the knee up and down and spreading her legs. Then let her feel the touch of your fingers.

Tease her with only your fingertips, moving closer and closer to her vagina, then retreating, and then try closing your fingers tight, tight, tight over her sensitive flesh. Many women love this love maneuver.

Now let your lips take over. Try touching them to her in tender caresses, closing them tight over her flesh in kisses seething with lust, and let her feel your tongue making her delectably wet. Try nipping her gently with your teeth, and let each touch, bite, or kiss move you a little closer to the ultimate erogenous zone—her inviting pink vagina.

$\mathcal{July}$ 11

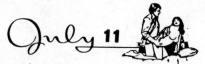

There are times when foreplay should be exactly that—play—so why not try this fun approach to sex tonight? You may just find that it excites her more than any serious effort you have ever made.

Take a large fluffy feather to bed with you (or have it there, waiting and ready) and playfully run it over her shoulders and throat, then, just as playfully, move it on down to her nipples. You will see them become erect at once. Take your time as you move on to her other erogenous zones, for teasing slowness is essential to the success of this little endeavor.

She may giggle and make a weak effort to attempt to stop you as you move that teasing feather over her navel, inner thighs, and if she twists and turns, her back and buttocks, but you can bet the giggle will be one of pleasure. As a finishing touch, try drawing the feather slowly through the cleft between her buttocks, a move that will cause her entire body to tingle with pleasure.

Then take her in your arms and let your love ease the tingling.

$\mathcal{July}$ 12

Here is a way to vary the side-by-side, partners-facing position for intercourse that will enable you to drive the full length of your penis in and out of her vagina far more easily, thus greatly increasing the pleasure for both of you.

It is best to begin with you lying on your back while she lies above you and places her legs outside your own as she settles down onto your penis. Wait until the two of you are locked together in the rhythms of sex, and then, with your arms tight around her, roll to one side. This will place you on your sides, with your body between her legs, her breasts against your chest, and you will be face-to-face, or better still, mouth-to-mouth.

Now slip one arm down and hook it under her leg, raising the leg until her knee is hooked over your elbow, and see how much easier it is to give her the full extent of that hardened penis she desires. This position also draws taut the muscles of the inner thighs, creating a sensation most women love, and she will demonstrate her love of it by twisting and writhing in reaction to each thrust of your penis.

Here is an exercise in sensuality that may not sound attractive at first, for it includes masturbation, but do not reject it for that reason; adult masturbation is more common than you might think, and it can be used to give you a better understanding of your own body, which, in turn, will make you a more gratifying lover.

Find a few moments of privacy just prior to being with her and lie comfortably on your back, in the nude, while allowing your mind to create sexual images of her that will give you an erection. Now masturbate to the point of climax—and stop.

Pause until the feel of approaching climax begins to fade, then repeat the process. Repeat it as many times as possible without reaching climax, then stop completely. You will find later, when you are with her, that your lingering sexual excitement is evident and arousing to her. This is but one of the ways masturbation can give you better control of your body and make you a better lover, and you will want to use the exercise often.

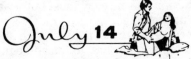

"The grass is always greener," they say, and this is why every woman, in some corner of her mind, harbors a desire to have love made to her by some unreachable male. You have secretly desired other women, too, and you know it. The object-persons may be movie stars, close friends, or simply the couple down the street, but the wish is there.

Tonight encourage her to fantasize upon that wish.

Tease her about some man whom you know she finds attractive, and pass along a little gossip about his sexual habits. (You can always create such gossip.) When she laughingly admits her desire, ask her what she thinks would take place if, suddenly, by some magic, she found herself in the arms of this man. She may not tell you, but later, as the two of you make love, this other man, without even knowing how you have used him, will be helping you to give her orgasm after orgasm. Fantasy, you see, is perhaps the greatest aphrodisiac of all.

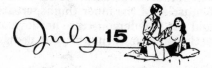

Ask her to go for a ride in your car. Have the windows open (or better yet, the top down, if you have a convertible), so the wind ruffles her hair, and drive just as fast as safety and the law will allow. Women, sometimes more than men, are pleasingly thrilled by speed and apparent recklessness. But they find boldness even more exciting.

So, when you are out into the country, reach over and, without a word, take her hand and place it over your groin. Then smile a smile of desire as you push her skirt high on her thighs, or press your fingers to the delectably soft center of her slacks. And start looking for a place to park. Her pleased reaction could very well make continued driving dangerous.

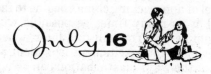

Tell her you are going to undress her using only your teeth, and defy her to do the same to you. It is no easy task, but it adds a bit of spice to the common act of undressing.

Your lips must necessarily brush against each and every part of her body as you tug your teeth at her bra, nylon and panties, causing her to purr with pleasure; and you will find her lips, as she bends to tug at your shorts, brushing repeatedly, by accident or intent, against your hardened penis. Could you ask for a better opportunity to show her that fellatio can be a mutually rewarding act?

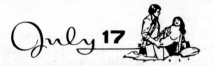

July 17

The so-called "missionary" position, in which the male lies full-length above the female while making love, has fallen out of favor in recent years—but it remains one of the better positions for those who put it to proper use. Use it properly tonight.

Let her enjoy the male hardness of your body touching hers as you drive your penis in and out of her clinging vagina; it is enjoyable for her to feel your hard chest against her soft breasts, your belly slapping hers, your legs pressing against her inner thighs. But remember to keep the full weight of your body off hers, as it is the one error that can destroy her pleasure, and let her enjoy the taste of your tongue in her mouth, your lips moving now and then to her nipples, and keep your hands moving constantly over her body.

Greater contact between your bodies is the essential ingredient of this old standby, so be sure to keep that ingredient active. It may make both of you want to give up your jobs and become missionaries.

July 18

Vaseline and K-Y jelly are the substances most commonly used to lubricate the anus prior to anal intercourse, but many women lose all desire during the pause needed to apply such lubricants.

So why not use the most natural lubricant of all to prepare her for anal penetration, and apply it in a way that will both stimulate her and silently signify your desire for anal intercourse? That lubricant is your saliva.

Hold her buttocks apart and lick the puckered circle of flesh until it is wet and relaxed by your caresses, then let your tongue lick as deep as possible into the anal canal. And she can, if she wishes, use her own mouth to wetten your penis prior to the moment of insertion. Though this "lubricant" does not provide the same ease of entry you gain with the others, it is enough, in most cases, and many anally oriented females prefer it—and that, of course, is because of the way it is applied.

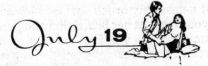

July 19

Take a deck of playing cards and secretly mark all the aces and the face cards, then tease her into playing a game of strip poker with you. Make up a betting system that will prolong the game, and let her select a sexual penalty that must be paid by the first to lose his or her clothes.

Then use your knowledge of the markings to beat the clothes off her. They say nobody likes a cheat, but this time she will love you for being one—and love you in a way she herself has chosen.

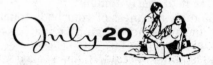

Every woman in this country is aware that she lives in a nation of breast-loving men. Yet it is a fact that few women, including those blessed with the most beautiful of breasts, are satisfied with the *size* of them. Many a woman with an exquisite bustline is convinced her breasts are too small, while, oddly, many women with large breasts are embarrassed by them. But all have one thing in common.

Every woman wants to believe her breasts are beautiful.

So tonight, as you hold those delectable spheres in your hands, as your lips draw her softly yielding flesh into your mouth and you flay her stiffened nipples with your tongue, let words of praise pour from your mouth. Use soft whispers to flatter the firmness, shape and beauty of her breasts, and avoid any mention of their size.

She may laugh and call you a flatterer, but you can safely bet she will want to hear every word . . . and more.

Try this variation of the common position for rear-entry intercourse and be prepared to hear her sigh with pleasure. It works best if the two of you are on a soft carpet with an armchair behind you.

Encourage her to kneel on the carpet while you kneel behind her, your knees between hers and her naked buttocks on a level with your erected penis. Lean over her, reaching under her body to fill your hands with her naked breasts, and enter her from this position. Wait until her naked buttocks writhe against your groin, then raise your body to an erect position, using your hands on her breasts to bring her with you. Now lean back until your shoulders rest against the armchair, drawing her body into a taut bow, and continue to move your penis. After a few moments, lean forward again, still driving your penis at her, but continue to draw her backward at regular intervals.

It creates in her body voluptuous sensations she may never have experienced—but she will want to experience them again and again and again.

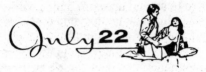

Offer to run her bath water for her.

Wait till she begins to prepare for her bath, tell her you will run the water, and do so—but make it scalding hot. Give her time to undress and make this discovery, then enter the bathroom and lock the door behind you.

Take her in your arms and warm her up while she waits for the water to cool. She'll love the delay.

The best way to help her shed her sexual inhibitions is to show her you have none of your own, so demonstrate this to her tonight.

Lead your conversation casually around to the topic of sexual inhibitions, and tell her there is no act you would not commit for her if you knew she would enjoy it—then defy her to name one she thinks you would not do.

But be prepared to back up your boasting!

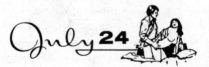

Here is a simple technique that will greatly intensify the pleasure of her orgasm, but you will have to let her know what you intend to do, and why, as the results are not so pleasant if she is unprepared. And besides, her anticipation of what you are going to do will add to the effect.

Have a container of ice close beside the bed as you kneel behind her to make love from a rear-entry position. When the faster writhing of her body warns you of her approaching orgasm (or when she tells you it is near), reach out and fill one hand with ice from the container.

Now drive the full length of your penis into her and, holding it there, suddenly place the ice against the upper edge of her vaginal area. She will moan with glee.

This is but one way in which a sudden change in temperature can be used to add pleasure to sexual orgasm, and it works equally as well in reverse, when she applies the ice to your testicles at the moment of climax. So why not mention that tonight?

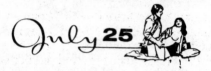

No woman should ever be forced to engage in any sexual act, but, strangely enough, many women derive immense excitement from the *impression* of force. This seems especially true with regards to fellatio. Find out how she reacts to this tonight.

Use your normal words and body signals (or your own oral skills) to encourage her to take your hardened penis into her mouth. Then, when her lips form a soft circle around its shaft, place your hands on the back of her head and begin driving your penis in and out of her mouth, straining to go deeper with each stroke. Slow down if she protests, or has real difficulty accepting it; but, if not, let your penis move faster and deeper with each stroke.

The violence of your thrusts will create a vague feeling of being forcibly "taken" which, to the experienced fellatrice, is often enjoyable; and if fellatio is fairly new to her, the same feeling may well cause her to develop into an eager oralist.

In either case, both of you come out ahead in the end.

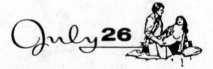

Take a few minutes to talk about the future. Ask her about her hopes, dreams, and plans, and tell her a little about your own future, as you see it . . . and let her hear you say that you see her as a part of your life in the years ahead.

Security is important to every woman, and every woman hopes for permanency in her relationship with a man. Even though the two of you, through marriage, may have made a lifetime commitment to each other, or, on the contrary, even if it was agreed that your relationship would involve no commitments, she still wants to hear you speak of her as part of your future. So say those words tonight. Make her feel loved and needed.

July 27

Convince her that you have slipped her an aphrodisiac.

Make her one of her favorite cocktails, wait until a few minutes after she drinks it, and ask her if she feels strange. Ask if she feels a tingling in her nipples, heat in her vagina. Then show her an empty packet of any type, tell her her drink was loaded with "Spanish fly" (this supposedly potent aphrodisiac is actually very dangerous and should be used under no circumstances; you mention it only because, like most people, she has heard the myths about it), and tell her she will soon be feeling its effects. Say that the pupils of her eyes are already dilated and the tone of her voice is strange. Tell her these are the first signs that the drug is working. Be convincing about this and you can bring into play the most powerful aphrodisiac in existence—the human mind; for if she believes you, the power of suggestion will actually cause her to feel uncontrollable sexual excitement. Be loving as you bring it under control.

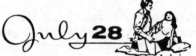

July 28

Would it surprise you to discover that she may like a bit of mild pain prior to, or along with, the act of sexual intercourse? Many women do have a degree of masochism in their psyche (which is probably why so many prostitutes allow themselves to be brutalized by pimps) and there is nothing wrong with this as long as it remains a secondary desire; that is, if the pain is mild and used to add to the pleasure of sex, not violent and the sole means of pleasure.

Find out whether she has such masochistic tendencies.

The way to do this is simple. Try playfully slapping her across the buttocks or the back of her thighs with a ruler or some similar object, not hard enough to make it sting. Make a game of it and do it several times, saying nothing of what you are trying to learn. Later, as you make love, if you find her urging you to nip at her earlobes, throat or breasts, to take her almost violently, you can be sure it is a delayed reaction to your earlier moves; and if not, you can always make it up to her by being especially tender with your loving.

July 29

Show her how *coitus interruptus* can be used for more than birth control! And show her how it can excite her beyond belief.

Tonight, when your driving penis has her writhing happily against you, her vagina growing warmer and wetter, and you yourself are nearing climax, abruptly withdraw your hardened shaft. Continue to caress and suck her nipples, perhaps changing your position, waiting until you feel able to control and withhold your climax, then enter her once again.

Repeated over and over, withdrawing your erected penis each time the crucial moment arrives, this process can make her literally hunger for the feel of your penis. When at last you do plunge it deep and hold it there while flooding her vagina with the warmth of your semen, her arms and legs will lock about you as if to hold you there forever.

Can you think of a better place to spend eternity?

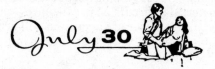

July 30

Any man can run one of those "John loves Mary" ads in the personal column of the local paper, but you can be different by slipping one past the editors and saying what you really want to say. Do it today.

Call your local paper and say you want to run an ad under the section dealing with horses (it is the farm section in some papers). This is the ad you place: "Young stallion offered for stud service," and include your name and phone number.

When it appears, call it to her attention, tell her you have decided to turn professional, and that you expect your fees to make you wealthy.

Then offer her a free sample that will show why your prices are so high and tell her you might even consider giving her a lifetime pass.

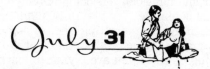

July 31

Take a little time today to make an objective study of your prowess as a lover. List on paper the number of positions you have used for sexual intercourse during recent months, the number of techniques you have tried. What, if anything, have you avoided because of inhibitions? How could your lovemaking with her be improved?

The answers, when set down on paper, will be far easier to appraise, and the results of this little test may surprise you. Keep those results and refer back to them in the months ahead, seeking always to improve on them. This will help you become the skilled lover she wants you to be.

August 1

Here is a little challenge you can make that, if she accepts, will prove even more exciting to her than to you. Make the challenge in a playful way and she will be more likely to take you up on it.

Tell her you do not believe that she can, without touching your body in any way, and without displaying her own body in an erotic manner, cause you to get an erection. This means she must try to arouse you by *talking* to you—and she may be bewildered by the results.

For as she begins, perhaps with a little mild sex talk, followed by, perhaps, a few descriptive phrases telling you what she would like to do to you, or what she fully intends doing to you, her words are going to be just as exciting to her as they are to you. Many women can become almost mesmerized in this manner, and you may find her violating the rules and defeating you by stripping away her clothing and using the sight of her naked body to bring you to erection.

The two of you can then test its hardness to satisfy yourselves that the contest is over.

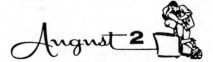

August 2

Tonight show her that anal intercourse can be the most exciting prelude to vaginal lovemaking she has ever known. It is the best way to make her fully aware of the pleasures analism has to offer.

Many women have a lower degree of anal eroticism than do others, and this type woman may dislike anal intercourse because it fails to bring her to orgasm, or, at best, your fingers or other means must be used as an adjunct to cause her climax. So try using a few moments of anal intercourse to arouse her, then switch to vaginal coitus to give her total fulfillment. Be sure to have a damp washcloth within easy reach, as the penis should always be washed when shifted from her anus to her vagina; for, although the anus is clean in most respects, it may contain bacteria that can cause vaginal infections.

So use your favorite position to make anal love to her, stopping and

105

withdrawing your penis to wash it quickly but thoroughly when you feel her arousal has reached its peak, then let her feel that hard shaft sliding across her clitoris as you suck and lick her breasts.

The same nerves of sexual reaction which make her clitoris the center of her sexuality extend to her anal canal, and as you thrust deep into her vagina, you will find that the prior anal contact has turned her into a delightful bundle of sexual desire. So try it!

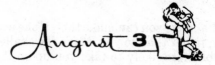

Today go shopping and buy her some sexy under-garments such as a pair of crotchless panties and a skimpy bra with openings over each nipple. Ask her to wear them while you make love. To wear such frilly underthings can be exciting to her, as well as to you, and, like many couples, you may develop a sexy little code that revolves around these items; by asking if she is wearing them (and you can do this in front of others, not letting them know what you mean), you will indicate your desire for sex; she can do the same by saying she has on the things you bought her, and only the two of you will know what she really means.

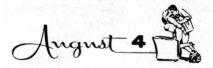

Here is a sex position that will add fun and variety to your lovemaking, so why not ask her to join you in a little fun tonight? The two of you sit facing each other, naked and ready, with your legs stretched out and parted. Her legs should be over yours. Have her slide forward so you can insert your penis deeply. Now place both hands on her shoulders, and have her place her own hands on yours. You are ready to go.

The two of you lean back simultaneously, your hands sliding down her arms and hers down yours, until you are leaning far back and holding hands. Let your hips twist for a moment, then slowly pull your bodies erect, so your lips can lock and you can feel her erected nipples against your chest. Lean back once more and repeat the process, and her face will soon take on a dazed expression as she savors the wonderful slowness with which your tumescent penis moves in and out of her vagina. Now, that is the kind of fun she likes!

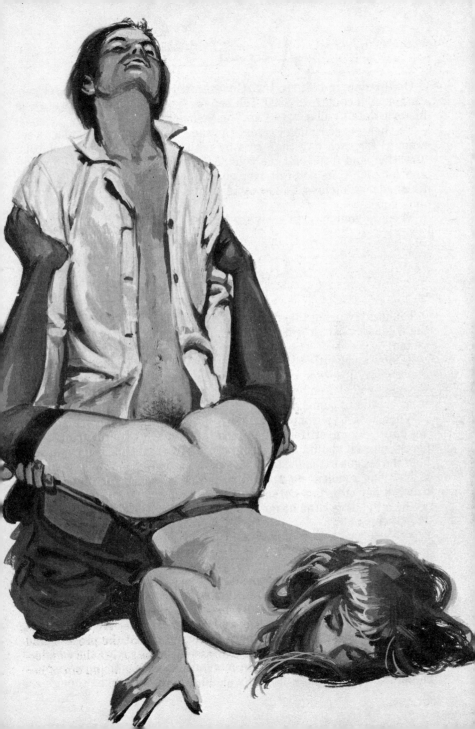

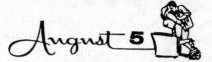

August 5

On this date in 1861 the U.S. Government imposed a tax of three percent on all income over $800. Tell her you have decided to celebrate this historic date by placing a "tax" on your lovemaking.

Tell her you are going to create a fund into which you will place a set amount for each day that goes by without some expression of your affection, and for each time your loving fails to bring her to orgasm, and for each time you roll over and fall asleep the moment you have finished making love. Tell her this will be hers to spend in any way she may choose.

Then do your best to keep her broke.

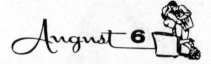

August 6

Tonight try using this delightful oral technique. It will bring her to the wildest, most violent orgasm either of you have ever seen, felt—or tasted.

Be slow and gentle with your kisses as you peel away her panties and move your lips ever closer to her naked vagina, for this planned slowness will stiffen her clitoris and put her in the proper mood for the treat that is to come.

When at last your mouth makes contact with the soft, moist flesh of her outer vagina, stiffen your tongue and force it between these sweet petals; move it about until you have located her stiffening clitoris. Now hold the tongue extended and move your head quickly from side to side, as if saying a violent no, and try to do this so swiftly that your tongue brushes her clitoris a dozen times a second.

She will answer the negative shake of your head with a loud cry of, "Yes, yes, *yes!*"

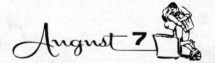

August 7

If you are like most men, you probably have a strong desire to have her swallow your ejaculated semen on those nights when she takes you into her mouth and fellates you; and if she is among a great number of women who allow old myths and misunderstandings to interfere with their sexuality, she has probably avoided doing this, even though she may secretly wish to try it and give both of you the added pleasure it may afford.

Begin tonight to help her overcome those inhibitions.

The way to do this is to let her know—by words and deeds—that you enjoy or even crave the taste of the juices that flow from her vagina when she is aroused. Show her this by covering her vaginal lips with your mouth and sucking greedily after you have brought her to orgasm, and tell her this as you take her in your arms after making love. It clearly shows that you expect or want her to do no more than you are willing to do.

Though the female does not actually ejaculate at orgasm, her vagina does flow hotly with lubricating fluids, and by swallowing these you are, in essence, performing the act you want her to try.

It may take awhile to work, but some night in the near future you may be pleasantly surprised to see her lips clinging to your throbbing penis while your hot, thick semen flows steadily down her throat.

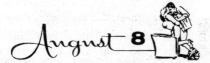

August 8

While rear-entry intercourse is extremely pleasurable to most women because of the greatly increased contact between penis and clitoris, its one drawback is that it usually denies her the thrill of having your lips suck and tug at her nipples, the excitement of feeling your tongue deep in her mouth. But there is a way to overcome this drawback, thus giving her the enjoyment of all these sexual components, so why not try it tonight?

Have her lie naked on her side while you hold her in your arms and press your naked body against her back and rear. Lift her leg and enter her from behind, just as you would do in the common side-by-side position for rear-entry intercourse. Let her feel a few strokes of your hardened penis before making the next move.

Now lift yourself up on one elbow and lean over her so you are able to use your lips to caress her throat and the side of her face; at the same time, use your hands on her breasts to encourage her to twist the upper part of her body toward you. Soon you will be able to lower your mouth to hers, and even better, to suck and lick at her firm, erected nipples, while continuing to drive your penis at her from the rear.

This turning of the body is far less uncomfortable for her than it sounds, though your own hip movements may be somewhat restricted, and any effort she is required to exert will be more than repaid by the pleasure you give her as you lovingly kiss and suck her breasts.

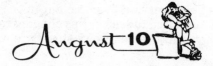

August 9

This is the age of equality of the sexes, and that means sharing a lot more than her bed. It means you should willingly accept your share of the less pleasant aspects of your relationship. So tonight, out of the clear blue sky, why not offer to do her laundry for her, either at home or at a laundromat?

This is a simple but boring task which most women hate, and she will love you for taking it off her hands. And you can spend your time beside that washer trying to anticipate the reward she is going to give you when the laundry is done.

August 10

Tonight use expert and swiftly moving fingers to bring her desires to new heights! This technique is one that drives many women absolutely wild. And she will drive you wild with her responses.

As you hold her in your arms and kiss her deeply, with your tongue reaching out to meet hers, use the thumb and forefinger of one hand to form a pincer and gently close it over the flesh of one of her breasts. With the other hand tweak the flesh of her buttock. Begin moving your hands rapidly over her body, repeatedly pinching the flesh of her inner thighs, stomach, breasts, and pubis, never letting her know where your fingers will be next. Vary the force with which you pinch her, but be careful not to cause her pain. She will soon be creating a pincer of her own—with her legs around your body!

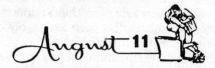

August 11

Cunnilingus is so satisfying to her because it is centered on her clitoris and your lips and tongue create a delicate friction against this tasty pink morsel and cause her to experience orgasm after orgasm, as long as contact and friction are maintained. But there is a technique of cunnilingus that is extremely arousing because it makes her even more eager for that first bit of clitoral contact. Why not try it tonight?

Have her lie on her back with her thighs parted, then you take a prone position between them, so you are looking directly at the soft fur and coral pink flesh of her vagina. Now use your thumbs to gently spread the labia, the soft outer lips of her vagina, and lay bare the pink flesh of her clitoris and its shaft. Stiffen and extend your tongue, then slowly begin to lick the inner flesh of the vaginal lips which your thumbs hold parted. Lick and lick and lick—but carefully avoid any contact with her stiffening clitoris. She will soon begin to twist and writhe in an effort to place it between your lips, perhaps pleading with you to suck it, and finally her hands will draw your face into the cleft of her wettening vagina.

Then you can suck that sweet little bud until both of you are satisfied.

The structure of our society is such that most of us have come to admire physical beauty more than the beauty of the inner person; we tend to imitate what the beautiful people do, and we are daily told, via TV and every form of advertising, that what is right for the beautiful people is right for us. It is a sad fact of life.

But there is a way you can turn this fact around and use it to help her overcome any inhibitions she may have, so why not put that way to use tonight? It will pay dividends on many nights in the future. Dividends for both of you.

Stop off at a bookstore and pick up a book filled with erotic photographs. Be sure it is one which depicts acts about which she is a little bit inhibited. Then take it home and share it with her.

If neither of you have seen such books recently, then you are in for a mutual surprise; the day is long past when only aging prostitutes and worn-out slatterns were willing to pose for erotic photographs, and today some of the most beautiful females imaginable are happy and eager to be photographed in the midst of fellatio, intercourse, analism, group sex, and every other erotic act the mind can conceive. This is certain to have its effect on the woman at your side. Not only will she be sexually aroused by these erotic illustrations but she will begin to see that such acts are participated in by girls so pretty, so beautiful in every physical sense of the word, that enjoyment of the act would appear to be their only possible motive, for most of these girls have the assets to make it as a "legitimate" model or actress.

And seeing this, she will be tempted to find out why—which means she will soon have one less inhibition. Or have none at all.

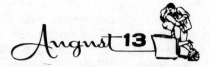

August 13

Give her a lick and a promise!

In the morning, as you are dressing to leave and she still lies in bed, or if this is not the situation, as she is dressing to go out, lean down to her vagina and slowly, teasingly, lick her with your tongue—once, and only once. Then give her the promise.

Tell her that was only a sample of what she is to get later, then smile, walk out of the room and close the door behind you. Her remembrance of the feel of your tongue and her desire for more will grow greater as the minutes and hours pass, and when the moment arrives, she will be eager and ready for the rest of the licks you promised.

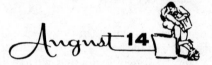

August 14

Lure her out into public; then, in a crowded elevator, bus, or the aisle of a department store—being absolutely certain no one sees you—run your hand lovingly over her buttocks or the back of her thigh; or if possible, stand behind her and suddenly let her become aware of your groin pressing against her rear.

There is little she can say or do in such a situation, of course, though she may give you a look that says she is peeved. But later you are likely to see her look change to one of desire, for most women like a little boldness and brashness in a man, and love the man who sometimes goes against society's "rules."

So try being a rulebreaker today.

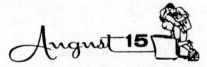

August 15

This position for cunnilingus may sound a little bit zany, a little bizarre, but that zaniness is one of the reasons many females find it so appealing. So give it a try tonight.

With your arms around her and the touch of your hands and lips on her naked skin driving her wild, lead her into a standing position behind a wide and comfortable armchair. Now lift her so that she sits on the back of it and then, holding her hands, have her lean backward until her shoulders are on the seat of the chair, her legs parted and her feet pointing up. Her vagina will be on a level with the back of the chair, bare and ready, and you need only lean down a bit to lick and kiss it. And you will find her growing hot and dizzy as you do—but it won't be because of the blood rushing to her head.

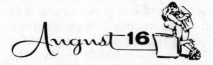

Here is an exercise in sensuality that every man should know and practice regularly, for it helps develop control over a movement of the tongue that, when used on her nipples, anus, or clitoris will fill her body with incredibly thrilling sensations. So try the exercise today and repeat it often.

Extend your tongue as far as possible, then move it in clockwise circles, about a dozen times, wetting as much of the area around your lips as possible. Now do the same in the opposite direction. Increase the number of repetitions each time you do this, trying always to reach a little further with the tongue, and soon it will become easy.

And it will be even easier when you do it to her.

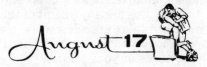

Perhaps you have noticed that active couples, those who share sports and recreation, seem also to be happier and more loving than their less active counterparts. That may very well be true because most sports involve a degree of physical contact, and it is only a short step from there to contact of a more intimate nature.

So ask her to play golf with you. Equipment can be rented, if you do not own it, and you would be surprised at how intimate the contact can become as you stand behind her, with your arms around her to correct her stroke; or, if she is the better player, as she stands behind you and gives you lessons.

One or two relaxing drinks at the "19th hole," a kiss or two when you reach home, and the two of you will be practicing strokes of a far different nature.

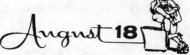

Oral-anal contact can be the most exciting part of sexual foreplay, and here is a technique so exciting, so delectable, that she is going to be teetering on the brink of orgasm long before she feels the first thrust of your hardened penis.

When she is eager, naked and ready, drop to your knees before her, as if getting ready to kiss and lick her vagina, then turn her in your arms so the creamy mounds of her buttocks are in front of you. Use both hands to spread these mounds and place your mouth to the cleft between them. Now extend your tongue and move it rapidly in a clockwise direction, so that it barely brushes the rubbery circle of her anus and wettens the flesh of the cleft of her buttocks; move your tongue in the opposite direction when she begins to twist, moan, and writhe. The tingling wetness left by your tongue will remain with her as the two of you make love, an exciting reminder of how skilled you are with your tongue, and she will be strongly tempted to try matching these skills the next time she is in your arms.

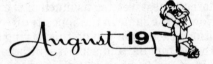

The basic reason a woman fellates a man is because she enjoys giving sexual pleasure to him, thus her enjoyment of this act is in direct proportion to your own. But there are a few ways in which you can add to her pleasure, so why not give some of them a try this evening? Both of you will reap the rewards of your efforts.

After encouraging her to fellate you, and getting her agreement to do so, ask her to kneel beside you on the bed, bending down to suck and lick your penis, and make it clear you want her to use this position because it will allow you to watch her lips and tongue moving over your erection, to enjoy the sight of her beautiful breasts and buttocks. Ask her to turn slightly and give you the added treat of being able to see and caress her naked vagina. There is a bit of the exhibitionist in us all, and she will derive some degree of excitement from this talk, and from putting herself on display for you.

As her lips begin to move over your erection, give her added pleasure by stroking her naked body, slipping your hand finally between her thighs and placing it over her vagina. Rub her there, letting the moves of your hand match exactly the speed with which her lips move up and down your penis. She may just reach orgasm long before you.

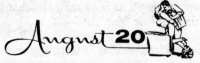

On this date in 79 A.D. Mt. Vesuvius erupted and totally destroyed

114

the ancient city of Pompeii. Recreate that famous eruption tonight on a minor scale.

Call her into the bedroom and show her the magnificent erection you have gained by thinking of her, tell her about the tragedy that took place on this day, and say you think somebody ought to remember it by triggering an eruption less destructive than the one that destroyed Pompeii. Tell her your hardened penis feels like a volcano about to erupt, and ask her to help you handle its explosion.

She most likely will. Lovers are very helpful when it comes to such matters.

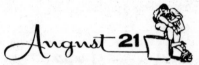

Make sex a little more exciting by first leading her to believe you have no intention of making love. It is a fine approach at times.

Tonight, when the two of you go to bed, give her a quick kiss, then turn onto your side, placing your back toward her. Wait a minute, and then, if she has not placed her arms around you and snuggled up close (the natural tendency is to do so), draw them around you. Give her another few moments, then, without a word, draw her hand down to your penis. She will take the next step.

It is very exciting to a woman to feel a penis growing hard within the grasp of her hand, and further excitement will be caused by the way the front of her body fits against the back of yours. Nature was wise enough to design the male buttocks so they fit very nicely into the incurve of the female groin, and as her hand begins to move slowly over the length of your erection, you will feel her hips begin to gyrate and press her mons against your rear.

That means it is time for you to roll over.

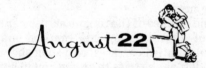

Tonight try a little sex treat that is almost certain to be tremendously exciting to you and is not going to be less than pleasing to her, as anything that increases the arousal of one partner almost always causes a similar reaction in the other. Approaching it in a joking manner will make it easier for her to accept, as is usually the case with any sex technique that sounds unusual or "far out."

Take a little snack to bed with you, and be sure it includes a bit of jam or other spreadable food. Be teasing in manner as you suddenly dab a bit of this over her bare nipple, but let your lips and tongue be utterly serious as you lick and lap it away. And carefully note her reactions as you do.

It is very common for a man to receive sexual stimulation through the ingestion of food or fluids taken from the female body, and many women are excited by allowing this to be done. It is less common for a woman to desire such ingestion, but not rare. So there is a chance that she may be only mildly excited by this act, or you may find yourself being asked to lick honey or whipped cream from the dish of her vagina, while she eagerly uses her lips and tongue to remove the same from your penis.

You'll never know unless you try.

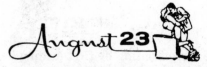

August 23

Here is a technique of cunnilingus that will cause any woman to experience orgasms so violent, so exquisite, that she will never forget the man who gave them to her. You be that man!

Have her lie on her back with her legs spread wide, her panties off, while you lie facing her naked vagina. Slip your up-turned palms under her naked buttocks, lifting them, and let her throw her legs over your shoulders, if she wishes. Get ready for her soft moans of pleasure.

Stiffen your tongue and place the tip of it between her vaginal lips, at the very bottom, and slowly, very slowly, lift your head and move your tongue up to the very top of her vaginal flesh, where the most sensitive parts are located. When you reach this point, move your head back about an inch, abruptly ending the contact, and do not touch her as you again lower your tongue to the very bottom of her vagina. Lick her again and again with this upward movement of the tongue, moving faster and faster, and inserting your tongue deep one time, scarcely touching her the next.

Unlike the rapid strokes of the tongue across her clitoris she receives in most types of cunnilingus, this method makes her wait and anticipate those delightful caresses, and soon she will be holding your face against her cleft as she tries to drown you in her hot vaginal fluids. What a lovely way to go!

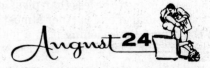

August 24

Here is a position for sexual intercourse that has become so popular among knowing couples that it is almost a classic. It is sometimes called the "wheelbarrow" position, and it is one the two of you are sure to love—after you try it tonight.

Have her kneel on the carpet while you kneel behind her, leaning over her as you enter her from the rear. Drive the shaft of your penis deep into her vagina, then hook your forearms around her thighs and slowly begin rising to your feet. This places her so her back is slightly arched, her weight resting on her hands or forearms, and her legs are around your body. You are holding her legs much like the handles of a wheelbarrow as you drive your hardened penis into her hot, wet vagina—and she will love each stroke!

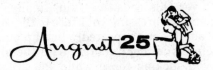

Some women wear "falsies" to fool the men around them, so why can't you use a similar trick to arouse her curiosity?

When she is not looking, take some hard object with a cylindrical shape and place it in your front trouser pocket, arranging it so that it looks like you have a huge erection. Then sit down and wait for her to notice it. Say nothing about sex, and try to keep from laughing; try to appear bored.

She will soon be staring at that hard swell, wondering what is causing it and why it refuses to disappear; and sooner or later, she will be tempted to touch it and see if it is real. That is when you smile and get rid of your "falsie" and produce the genuine article.

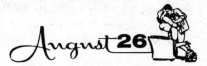

Would you believe that the position you choose for sleeping can have a tremendous effect on your sex life? Well, you had better believe it, and tonight is the night to prove to yourself how it works.

After you have finished making love, give her a kiss and a smile, then turn on the bed, so your face rests on her thighs, or is very near her vagina, and tell her you intend sleeping there so the first sight to greet you in the morning will be that delectable part of her body. And *do* sleep there.

Nothing beats sex in the early morning—unless it is sex that lasts from late evening till early morning—and the first of you to open his or her eyes is going to be greeted by a sight that tempts the beholder to begin where you left off on the night before. Begin!

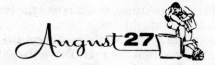

August 27

Her nipples are an erogenous zone you know all about, of course, but are you also aware that the firm, sleek flesh directly beneath them, the flesh on the delectable undercurves of her breasts, is one of her most potent sexual regions. Find out how potent tonight.

Try cupping your hands beneath the delightful mounds of her breasts and exerting a steady upward pressure that causes your hands to slide slowly over this sensitive skin, finally brushing over her erected nipples; and try pressing your face to the soft underside of her breast, letting your tongue repeatedly lick up over the sweet globe, stopping just before you make contact with the nipple.

Let her feel you sucking those while you are driving at her the hardened penis she is soon going to demand of you.

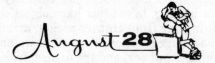

August 28

Ask her to go with you to the nearest college or university and count the streakers. Streaking, as you probably know, is the fad in which nude students dash madly through public places, and she will be amused at the idea and eager to go.

You may or may not spot any streakers, but you will have put her in a playful frame of mind and directed her thoughts to the subject of nudity.

Play your cards right and soon you will be streaking toward the bedroom.

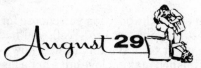

August 29

Here is an oral technique that works exceptionally well when you are above her, in the famous "69" position, and looking down on her delectable vagina.

After a few preliminary touches with your lips and tongue, use your fingers to gently spread her labia (she may want to do this for you unless her hands are already occupied with your penis and testicles) and stiffen your tongue as you slip it between those petals of flesh.

Bob your head quickly up and down over her vagina, sliding your stiffened and extended tongue quickly in and out of her dewy flesh, using it as if it were a small, wet penis. Nothing you can do will give her more encouragement to open her lips and give equal wetness to that "other" penis, the real one that is hot and hard above her face.

Why not try it tonight?

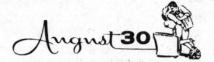

August 30

You are probably aware that the mild bit of pain you create when you nip at her breasts, buttocks, and inner thighs adds much to her sexual pleasure, but do you also know that she can receive similar stimulation by inflicting such mild pain on *you?* Give her the opportunity to try it tonight.

During the foreplay, when first her lips move to the lobes of your ears or the hollow of your throat, when first those lips—or her teeth—close strongly over your skin, let her know you find it pleasing and encourage her to cover your body with nipping little kisses. You will find they stoke the fires of your passion, and from this beginning she will reach a height of arousal that has her clawing at your back and gasping her love as she writhes in orgasm.

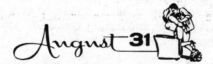

August 31

The position you choose for anal intercourse can be just as important to the pleasure of it as it can be to any other act, so why not ask her to try this position tonight? It is one she may ask you to use often.

After she has removed the last of her clothing and her anus has been lubricated with K-Y jelly or another lubricant, lie naked on your back and have her kneel above and facing you, with one knee on each side of your body, as if preparing for coitus but with her vagina poised a little higher over your pubis. Use one hand to hold your erection so it is directly under her anus, have her reach down with both hands and spread her buttocks, and she can then lower herself onto your hardened shaft . . . and lift herself and lower herself, etc., etc., etc.

September 1

Few men really know how to ask a woman to perform fellatio, or to encourage her to do it without being asked. She may actually long to feel your hard penis filling her mouth, causing her lips to pucker around it, yet it is highly unlikely she will place it there until she receives the proper signal from you. And it must be proper. Even the experienced and sometimes eager fellatrice may be turned off by a man who ignores her desires and sensitivites when making it known he wants her to perform oral sex. Avoid doing that.

The best way to request oral sex, it almost goes without saying, is to perform oral sex on her, and the classic "69" position for simultaneous licking and sucking is best, along with any side-by-side variation. Your hard penis is there and ready for her to take, but never make the mistake of forcing it against her face or trying to lift her head against it, as this may increase any reluctance she feels; instead, try reaching back and guiding her hand to your testicles and the hard shaft of your penis while letting your tongue and lips remain busy on her vagina. The feel of your hardened penis in her hand can be very exciting, and if the tongue with which you lick and lap her is skillful, you are very likely going to feel that hand guiding your penis to the wet velvety warmth of her mouth.

So why not join the "Oral Signal Corps" tonight?

September 2

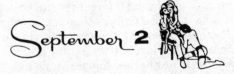

Do you remember the first time you engaged in heavy "petting" with a girl? The first time your hand made contact with that fluffy hair and warm moist flesh you came to love so well? The way you slipped one finger in the soft folds of flesh and then moved it rapidly back and forth, certain in your own mind that you were giving her the thrill of her young life? Well, you probably weren't.

That is the way most young boys try to stimulate a girl (they can get away with it when the girl is so inexperienced that she finds any touch

120

arousing), and if you still use this method as a part of foreplay, it is time you learned a better way. Many women dislike having a finger actually inserted into the vagina, some literally cannot stand it, and only a minority prefer it above all other methods.

Tonight, when first your fingers reach that delightful area in your attempts to arouse her, try letting them form a cup over her mons, the semi-firm mound above her vagina, and move this gently from side to side, up and down, and in circles until she begins to respond. The pressure you apply here will act directly on her clitoris, causing it to rise and make itself ready for the touch of your fingers, and that touch should be light as a feather, for anything more can be painful.

Contrary to popular opinion, few women actually "insert a finger to search for the clitoris" when they masturbate, and many, perhaps most, bring themselves to orgasm solely by manipulating the mons. You should remember that your vaginal caresses are the equivalent of masturbation, and act accordingly when she is in your arms tonight.

September 3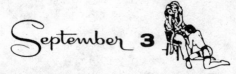

Tonight give up a little of your own pleasure in order that you may multiply hers. And plan on going to sleep late.

Stop by a drugstore and buy one of those delaying creams of the type used to prevent premature ejaculation. There are many brands on the market, and you have probably seen them advertised in magazines or sold in vending machines. They work by making the strategic areas of the penis less sensitive, but most men are able to maintain an erection while wearing them.

Follow the instructions on the package and apply a bit of this to your penis before you begin to make love. The slight numbness will cause the first minutes of copulation to be a little less exciting for you, but as those minutes begin to add up, you will find her reaching orgasm after orgasm due to the prolonged thrusting of your hardened penis.

And your own climax, when finally it comes, will be a sensation!

September 4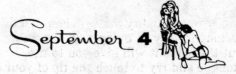

Love is the world's best aphrodisiac, and each expression of love from you will arouse her as nothing else can do, so why not take a few minutes to write her a love letter.

Write as if you were talking to her. Mention a few reasons for your love, a few of her character traits, and recall a few things that have occurred in the past. Promise her better things in the future.

Drop it in the mail today. Since the Postal Service is a trifle slower than the old Pony Express, you have absolutely no way of knowing when she will receive it. But when that day arrives, and she has read your letter, she will tip you off by taking you in her arms for an even better expression of love.

September 5

If you think a variety of oral techniques is important only when you lie licking, kissing, and sucking her vagina, then you are mistaken; for she wants you to show just as much skill when your mouth moves to cover her breasts. Here is a delightful technique you can try tonight. It will have her quivering in your arms.

When her bra is off and those smooth mounds are naked before your eyes, spread your fingers wide and encircle as much of the soft flesh as you can, holding it so your thumbs are under her breasts. Now let your hands lift gently upward and outward, at the same time closing the circle made by each hand, so that a small peak of flesh, tipped by the berry of a nipple, is visible between the thumb and first finger of each hand.

Now take one of these peaks into your mouth, sucking it steadily but gently, until it is warmly wet, then use the tip of your tongue to flick the erected nipple rapidly up and down. Her other nipple, when your mouth moves to cover it, will be firm and stiff; and as your lips and tongue move back and forth, from nipple to nipple, her cries of pleasure will be a delight for you to hear.

September 6

Here is an exercise in sensuality that will help you drive her into ecstasy with your tongue. Try it today and remember to practice it often—and to put the skills it will give you to use.

Extend your tongue and try to touch the tip of your nose. You will probably be unable to do so at first, but make a least a dozen attempts. Then try to touch your chin, once again making at least a dozen attempts. These movements will come easier with practice, and you can easily imagine what they will do to her. They will drive her delirious with ecstasy.

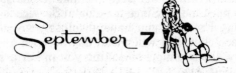

September 7

Take her camping while the weather still permits, and make the trip a real "love-out."

Rent equipment, if you do not own it, and take her to the most romantic spot you know. Choose a campsite that will allow you to enjoy plenty of privacy . . . and make the most of it.

Nights are a little cool now, which will encourage her to sleep close to you, and there is something very special about making love in a secluded spot with the smells and sounds of the forest around you, the dim light of a campfire casting shadows on the walls of a tent. Find out what is so special about it.

September 8

Standing positions for sexual intercourse are among the most exciting of all, and here is a way the two of you can make a good thing even better. So much better that she will ask you to do it often. Be obliging!

When the two of your are naked and ready for sex, stand facing her and slip your hands under her buttocks, supporting her as she lifts her legs and locks them around your body, settling her warm vagina over your hard erection at the same time. Now have her cling to your neck while you move your hands from her buttocks to her upper arms, then have her lean back, as far away from you as she can manage. Use your grip on her arms to lift her up once again, kissing her while her breasts tease your naked chest, and have her lean back once more.

Each time her upper body moves away from you, her weight must shift and press her mons tight against your upper groin, her vagina must swing in to swallow the full length of your hardened penis. She will love each moment of it.

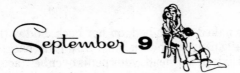

Let your tongue transform her into a bundle of love!

Cunnilingus can be its most delectable best when she is in the position you are going to ask her to assume tonight, so don't hesitate to ask her to assume it; you will never again have to ask, for this is certain to become one of her favorites.

Have her lie on her side, naked and ready for the touch of your tongue, and draw her knees up against her breasts, hugging them with her arms. This places her in something very similar to the fetal position, only much prettier.

Lie on your side, behind and below her on the bed, so your face is close to the delectable flesh between her thighs. To reach this flesh you will have to press your face tight against the backs of her thighs and lower buttocks—a little extra she will love—and extend your tongue to its fullest as you begin to lick her. But wait till you see how she reacts to each lick!

Touch your tongue as far toward the upper or front part of her vagina as you can reach and let it flutter wildly as you move back toward her rear. Let her feel it moving over the rearmost parts of her vagina, up into the cleft between her buttocks, and once again toward the front of her loins. Terrific!

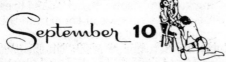

Drop an ice cube down the front of her blouse or sweater, and do your best to keep it there while she struggles to get it out!

This is a playful way to start a little horseplay that involves a lot of physical contact, and you can bet she will be promising vengeance as the two of you struggle to decide the fate of that cube of ice. Think of the logical place for her to attack with her ice as she seeks revenge, and you will realize that the physical contact is going to become much more intimate.

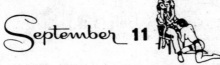

Try this position for oral sex . . . and be prepared for some very pleasant results!

Have her lie naked on the bed, on her back, and with her head over the edge, so she can, when she wishes, throw it far back. You stand with one leg on each side of her head, your penis over her face, and place your hands beside her hips for support as you lean far forward and begin to kiss, lick, and suck her quivering vagina.

And why was she asked to lie with her head over the edge of the bed? Because when her head is thrown far back, the muscles in the throat are moved in a way that allows her to more easily accept the full length of your hardened penis. This ease of acceptance can only make the act of fellation more enjoyable for her, as you may discover when you feel the warm circle of her lips clinging greedily to the very base of your shaft.

September 12

Sexual intercourse, you know, is much more enjoyable to her when her vaginal fluids are flowing freely and her flesh is thoroughly lubricated prior to the first penetrating thrust of your erected penis. Assure her of that pleasure—and more—by using this little bit of artistry.

Have a bottle of baby oil on hand as you prepare to make love, and tease her into letting you apply some to her naked breasts and stomach so you can enjoy the added sleekness of them (and they really will feel incredibly good against your naked body).

Now, as you apply the oil to her stomach, tilt the bottle over the top of her naked pubes and "accidentally" spill a bit of it there, being sure it flows over her vaginal lips and the region of her clitoris. Pretend to rub it away with your fingers while actually making sure it covers as much of her flesh as possible.

Baby oil is used as a lubricant by many women who masturbate, it feels incredibly good as it flows over the vagina, is absolutely safe, and will have her whimpering with pleasure as the two of you make love.

September 13

Do you think she would be offended if you used trickery to get her to place her hand unwittingly on your penis? It is highly doubtful that she would. Most women like a man who sometimes takes a playful approach to sex, and it is a rare woman indeed who is not excited by physical contact with a man's penis. So why not use a little trickery tonight?

Wearing an old pair of trousers from which you have cut away one of the front pockets, and holding in both hands some items that are useful for little more than filling your hands, ask her if she would mind reaching in your pocket and getting your car keys. Let her feel around until she realizes the item she is touching is much bigger, hotter, and harder than a set of keys.

Then drop whatever you are holding and fill your hands with *her!*

September 14

On this date in 1814 Francis Scott Key wrote the words to "The Star-Spangled Banner," our national anthem. Be sure to remind her of this, and mention also that it is traditional to stand as a show of respect for this song.

Then suggest that you celebrate by making love while standing!

She may think you are a little bit zany, overly patriotic (or *un*patriotic), but she will go along with the suggestion if you call her attention to the fact that your penis is already standing at rigid attention in honor of this day.

Can you think of a more unique way of suggesting sex?

September 15

Ask her to read you a bedtime story—of the sort that will put neither of you to sleep!

Select a chapter from a good erotic novel (be sure it includes a type of sex you think she would enjoy) and talk her into joining you on the bed and reading it to you. Let her get well into an arousing portion of the book, and then, while she continues to read the descriptive phrases, begin intimately stroking her breasts, thighs, and pubes. She will soon want to do more than read about sex.

Good erotica is arousing to most women, and reading it aloud, hearing one's own voice utter vivid descriptions of the various sex acts contained in these books, can be especially stimulating. Even more so because you are there to hear them and to stroke her eager body with your hands.

$\mathcal{S}$eptember 16

Those battery-operated massage devices that strap on the back of the hand may be used in many ways to excite her and bring her to shaking, quivering orgasm, and this is one of the best. These relatively inexpensive devices are a tremendous asset when it comes to sex, so if you don't already own one, today is the perfect time to buy. And tonight is the perfect time to use it.

Have her stand naked in front of you while you caress each and every part of her body with the hand wearing the vibrating device, kneeling to run your tingling fingers up each of her legs, rising to stroke her stomach and breasts, and circling her with your other arm as you kiss her lips and reach around to massage her buttocks.

Now hold her body against yours, your tongue flickering deep in her mouth, and cup the fingers of the hand wearing the vibrator under her vagina, so they are touching the lips and your palm is against her mons. Hold the hand there, unmoving, while she clings to your penis and sucks at your tongue. Soon her hips will begin to pump, slowly at first, then faster, and you will feel her grow wet as she reaches the first in a series of orgasms that will continue long after your hard, throbbing penis has entered her.

$\mathcal{S}$eptember 17

Are you one of those men who feel capable of only one climax? And do you sometimes get the feeling that you would be a more satisfying lover if you were capable of more? Well, you are capable of more, and tonight is the night to prove it—to yourself and to her.

After you have finished making love for the first time, spend a few moments close beside her, simply enjoying her presence while the two of you rest a bit, then try this little experiment.

Place one hand over her vagina and begin lazily caressing it, stroking the mound above it, letting your fingers close in a loving pincer over it outer lips. Then let your caresses become a little bit more aggressive—and then a lot more!

Few men realize that at this moment while the vagina is pleasantly warmed by the ejaculated semen, after the hard and stroking penis has brought her to orgasm (which it did, unless you have not been paying attention to this book), a woman remains highly susceptible to sexual stimulation. Your hands will soon have her writhing with desire, you will be exciting yourself as you toy with her soft, moist loins, and she will use her own hands and lips to give you all the help you need in order to regain that wilted erection. You may be pleasantly surprised to discover that, now, more than at any other time, she will be happy to take your penis in her mouth and suck it till it becomes a steel-hard rod capable of satisfying her own desires.

So use it to satisfy them!

September 18

Do you always dive right in there when you perform cunnilingus? Well, if you do, you are denying her one of the most pleasurable parts of the act, and denying yourself the pleasure of giving it to her.

Tonight give her a thrill she may have been missing.

As you kneel over, or in front of, the delectable sweet puff of her vagina, let her feel your breath playing over the smooth skin surrounding it. Kiss and lick her inner thighs, making them tingle, and then blow lightly on her vaginal lips. Kiss these lips softly pause, and blow on them once again. Let her feel your breath ruffling her soft pubic hair, moving repeatedly over the petals of her flesh, and then, finally, when she writhes before your eyes, let her feel your tongue lapping her juices.

Your breath can add greatly to the effect of your cunnilingus, so take this opportunity to put it to use.

September 19

Ask her to do something exciting for you—then surprise her with results that are twice as exciting to her!

Guide her into any of the female-above positions for sexual intercourse and wait until she has settled herself onto the shaft of your erected penis before beginning this adventure.

Now take her hand and guide it down to the soft and hairy mound at the top of her pubis and ask her to press against this with her fingers as the two of you move together; tell her it creates wonderful sensations in your throbbing penis, which, indeed, it will.

But as you continue to drive your erected shaft in and out of her velvety flesh, you will see her fingers begin to move and a dazed expression indicative of orgasm come over her face, for her fingers know just what is needed to fill her body with delights beyond belief . . . and she will use them to do just that!

September 20

Give this position a try tonight. She will remember it for many, many nights to come.

When the two of you are stripped to beautiful nudity and she is as eager as you for love, place a hassock a few feet in front of a narrow chair, spacing them so you can lie with your upper back and shoulders resting on the hassock and have your feet and legs supported by the chair. Have your legs together.

She can now stand with one leg on each side of your body and lower herself at will onto the hard, upright shaft of your penis, taking as much or as little of it into her body as she may desire—though you are likely to find she desires it all.

September 21

Ask her to try a little experiment in ESP, and then use your own common sense to pave the way for a truly great night of lovemaking!

Tell her you want her to sit quietly and concentrate on the one sex act she would most like to try if she were totally free to do so, and tell her you are going to read her thoughts and guess what it is. Ask her to tell you if you guess correctly, but assure her that she is free to keep it to herself if she so desires.

Then keep her thinking about this for as long as you can. It makes little difference what your guesses are, or how close to the truth they come; it is important only that she think hard about the sex fantasy her mind has created.

We all use fantasy, to a varying degree, to increase our enjoyment of the sex act, and by urging her to think strongly of a sex act in which she would like to engage (or has engaged), you will have turned her thoughts in a direction that will lead to some fabulous lovemaking later on.

It may even be the kind she was thinking about.

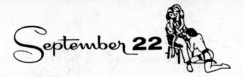

September 22

Cunnilingus, in slang, as you probably know, is generally referred to as "going down on a woman," and one of the best oral techniques is one in which, aptly, you do exactly that.

So why not thrill her this evening by showing her how this act of love got its common name? That common name also describes fellatio, you know, and she may just decide to reciprocate.

Have her lie naked on her back, with her thighs parted, while you move over her, taking much the same position you might assume for simultaneous fellatio and cunnilingus. Now slip your hands under the small of her back and lift her vagina toward your face, so the weight of her body rests on her shoulders and upper back. Stiffen your tongue and begin the motions of "going down."

Keep your tongue stiff and straight as you lower your face to her pubis, and then begin bobbing your head so that your tongue stabs quickly into her vagina, withdraws, and stabs again. She will react to each stab as if it were an arrow from the quiver of Cupid.

September 23

Tonight show her one of the many ways in which anal intercourse may be made more thrilling for her. That also makes it more thrilling for *you*.

Indicate to her that you have anal intercourse on your mind this evening, get her agreement, strip away her clothing, and use a good lubricant on her anus so entry will be easier to achieve. Have her kneel on the bed while you stand or kneel behind her, and let her feel your hands and penis caressing her naked buttocks as you prepare to enter her. Then give her a surprise by entering her vagina instead of her anus. The fact that she does not expect this pleasure will make it even greater.

Soon she will be slowly undulating before you, moving closer to orgasm with each thrust of your hardened penis, and her pleasure will continue when you suddenly shift your penis from her vagina to her rearmost orifice.

The continued thrusting of your penis through that even tighter tunnel of flesh may by itself bring her to orgasm, or she may need to feel your hand stroking her mons and clitoris, but you can be sure she will enjoy the anal experience as never before.

September 24

Standing positions for sexual intercourse are many and varied, and here is one of the very best variations. Why not share it with her tonight?

When she is naked and ready for sex, stand close before her and slip your arms around her, lifting and holding her, as she lifts her legs, one at a time, and throws them around your waist. When your loins are locked with hers, take a few steps (this creates some terrific sensations!) and place her back against a wall. Press your hips strongly into the warm cradle formed by her thighs, grinding your pubis against hers, and alternate this with long strokes of your penis. She will love it!

September 25

Try this tremendously pleasing technique of cunnilingus tonight, and expect to lie with your face between her thighs for a very long time, as she is going to want more and still more of this.

When she is on her back with her panties off, her sleek thighs parted, and you are between them, your face so close that your breath is hot on the outer flesh of her vagina, extend your tongue and hold it so that it barely touches the pink flesh of her vaginal lips.

Now begin moving your tongue in a slow circle, letting it brush the dewy surface of her flesh, but being careful not to penetrate between the lips. Try to make the circle so wide that it caresses all of her outer flesh, and vary the direction of it. You will soon see her labia parting, her clitoris swelling to seek contact with your tongue, and hear her purring with pleasure. This slow, deliberately light licking is a type of cunnilingus she will love.

September 26

Her tactile senses are the ones to which you should devote most of your attention, for the sense of feel is the center of sexual enjoyment. And just as certain of her silk and nylon undergarements arouse you with their sensuous feel, so, too, can certain materials be used to increase her sexual excitement. Try this one tonight.

Have a scarf of fine silk beside you as the two of you prepare to make love. When she is thoroughly aroused and utterly naked, take the scarf in your hand and spread it lightly over the dome of her breast. Now cover both the scarf and the peak of her breast with your mouth and use the tip of your tongue to flog her erected nipple.

Move the scarf down to her pubis, your lips following, and let her feel it teasing her inner thighs in the last seconds before you lock your lips over the thin veil and drive her into a sexual frenzy by licking and sucking her through it. As a final touch, just before you move over her for intercourse, fold the scarf and draw it slowly through the cleft between her buttocks. Delectable!

September 27

You almost certainly know that many women love having sexual intercourse while covered, or nearly covered, with water, but have you considered the many things that may be done to make this "water sport" even more enjoyable? Consider this one.

Have her lie naked in a tub containing enough warm water to completely cover the curves of her naked body, and let your hands explore each of those curves as you join her in the tub. Wait until your penis moving in her vagina causes her to twist and writhe underneath you and then open the drain.

As the level of the water slowly falls around her naked and gyrating body, letting her feel the different temperature of the air touching her skin, her awakened senses will cause her to react with increasing excitement to each thrust of your hardened penis.

September 28

Ask her to spend the day—or at least a large part of it—in mutual nudity. She will likely agree, for nudity can be just as exciting for her as for you, and is practiced in the home by many couples.

Nothing strips away pretenses and inhibitions faster than does total nudity, and you may find that it strengthens your relationship by making it more honest and open.

It will certainly make it easier to enjoy the physical aspects of your relationship.

$\mathcal{S}$eptember 29

The way you kiss can be the most important part of your sexual foreplay. It can excite her beyond belief, or leave her cold and unresponsive. The latter will occur less often if you know and use a wide variety of kisses, so try adding this one to your arsenal.

When first you take her in your arms and press your mouth to hers, have your lips slightly parted; but instead of thrusting your tongue deep into her mouth, which is not always exciting to all women, extend only the tip of your tongue and move it rapidly from side to side between her lips. It is a very suggestive kiss, and soon you will feel her own tongue matching the action of yours. A little bit more and her hips also will match the action of yours.

$\mathcal{S}$eptember 30

Try burning a little incense in the bedroom prior to making love! The heady aroma of many of these scents is stimulating to the erotic impulses, and this is one of the few ways in which the sense of smell may be brought into action during sex. You may be surprised to discover that it makes the act of love a more total one.

$\mathcal{O}$ctober 1

One small move or gesture on your part can sometimes add a new excitement to even the most common sex position, and tonight is the night to make your move with her.

Here is the move to make.

As the two of you begin making love, place yourself over her in the common male-dominant position and enter her as you would normally do. Wait until her hips begin to roll in response to the thrusts of your penis.

Now suddenly and without a word grasp both her wrists in your hands and hold her arms pinned to the bed above her head. At the same time begin driving your penis at her with all your strength, and, if she usually responds favorably to mild, teasing pain, nip at her throat, earlobes, and breasts with your teeth.

This creates an illusion of being ravaged, of being forcibly taken, perhaps even raped, and this illusion will create excitement in her because the fantasy of being raped is the most common of all among females. The fantasy is a relative of the wish, and this is one of the many ways it can be used to increase her sexual pleasure.

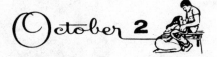

October 2

Does it surprise you to hear that her arms can be a source of sexual stimulation? It shouldn't. Those Continental lovers who were portrayed in so many movies of yesteryear, the ones who bent to kiss the hand of a lady and then let their lips stray up her inner forearm, knew exactly what they were doing.

Find out what they were doing, and find out tonight.

As you hold her in your arms during foreplay, or while you are making love, take her hand in yours and draw it to your lips. Let your tongue flicker wetly over the tips of her fingers and the palm of her hand, and move your lips and tongue slowly, caressingly up her inner arm—all the way up!

You can ignore her shivers, for they will be shivers of delight.

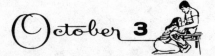

October 3

Here is an oral technique that combines several types of stimulation, and she is sure to love each and every one. And she will love you for giving them to her. What woman wouldn't?

When your stroking hands and caressing lips have aroused her to the point of no return, have her lie on her back with her thighs parted and her vagina naked and ready to receive the loving you have promised. Take a prone position before her and lift her legs so they fall across your back. Slip one hand under her buttocks and place the other over her mons, that pleasure-giving mound above her vagina.

Let your tongue lick her slowly at first, not going deep into her vagina but merely teasing her outer flesh, and use your hand to gently massage her mons; move it up and down, from side to side, and in circles. These are the motions of female masturbation, and soon her hips will begin to roll and undulate. That is when you begin to use the hand you placed under her buttocks.

Still licking her slowly and lovingly, still masturbating her, gently slip one finger of this hand between her buttocks and press the tip of it against her anus. Maintain a steady but gentle pressure, and let it slip into her only if her reactions tell you that is what she wants, which they probably will. Keep your other hand busy, your tongue and lips even busier, and soon her body will arch upward as she pleads with you to continue and increase the tremendous delights you are giving her. So continue and increase.

Take her for a motorcycle ride. You don't have to own or rent a motorcycle to do it; simply stop by a dealer's and tell him you want to test-drive one. He will be glad to let you.

The motorcycle industry has used a type of advertising that causes most people to associate these vehicles with masculinity, and many women are sexually aroused by riding them, by feeling the wind in their hair while that powerful motor beats between their thighs. And, of course, she will be riding with her arms around you, her breasts pressed against your back, perhaps, even, with a hand in your lap.

And don't feel you are cheating the dealer. There is always the chance you will like this so well you decide to buy, and that is what he is hoping for.

Buy a small jar of lotion—any old kind will do—and transfer it to a medicine bottle. Have the bottle in your hand and a sad look on your face when you walk through the door, and tell her you have just been informed by the doctor that you are suffering from a rare but noncontagious skin disease. Tell her the lotion is to be applied to your body—all of your body—and ask her if she would mind putting it on for you.

Wait until she has done so, and you are naked on the bed, and then smile as you inform her that the only thing from which you are suffering is the erection she can clearly see.

That is an affliction she knows how to cure.

October 6

On this date in 1863, in Brooklyn, a certain Dr. Shephard opened the first Turkish bath in this country. What better reason do you need to ask her to join you in taking one of these? And can you think of a more origianl way to ask her to remove her clothes?

To fill your bathroom with steam, thus converting it into a "Turkish" bath, run a little very cold water into the tub and then run scalding water into this. Have fluffy towels (hot from the dryer if possible) with which to briskly rub your bodies as you soak up the steam, and have a comfortable place for loving close at hand.

For when she is overcome by the luxurious tingling caused by the steam and the towels (not to mention the sight of your naked body), you are certainly going to need one.

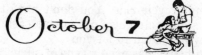

October 7

Sexual fetishism is a very odd thing. Fetishes of one type or another are more common among men than you might think. But it is extremely rare for a woman to have a sexual attachment to any item, material, or part of the body, to the extent that it can properly be described as a fetish. But what is odd is that many women are excited by catering to male fetishism, especially if it involves adoration of their bodies, or gives them a chance to create added excitement by dressing in a way that enhances the beauty of their bodies.

So let her help you indulge your "fetish."

Pick out a few of the most exotic items of clothing she owns—high-heeled shoes, leather boots, opera hose, whatever really excites you—and ask her to wear these and nothing else while you are making love. Tell her you have long dreamed of making love to her while she is dressed (undressed?) in this manner, and let the lust show on your face when at last she stands sexily posed before you. Be trembling with eagerness as you take her in your arms. She is excited by giving excitement to you, and the night will be a great one for both of you.

You may conclude those boots were *not* made for walking.

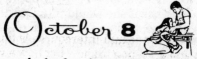

October 8

Tonight add a new dash of excitement to one of the most common positions for rear-entry sexual intercourse. A bit of spice always makes the good even better, and this is among the best of all spices.

Have her assume a kneeling position on the bed, her naked buttocks toward its edge, while you stand behind her. Enter her and begin making love as you normally would from this position, but lean far over her and slip your hands under her breats, cupping them.

Now slowly bring your body erect, using your hands on her breasts to bring her with you, and continue to drive your penis in and out of her vagina. After a few moments let her resume the kneeling position from which she started, continue to drive your erected penis at her, and then lift her upper body once again. For every action, according to the laws of physics, there is an equal and opposite reaction; in this case, when her upper body is drawn up and back by your hands, the reaction is a forward shifting of her pelvis that will increase the contact between penis and clitoris and have her writhing in ecstasy.

Which, she will agree, is worth bending over backward for.

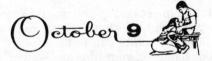

October 9

Tonight try a little method of cunnilingus that involves only the use of your lips, but is so exciting she won't even wonder why you are not using your tongue. She will just wonder why you have made her wait so long for this.

As you lie between her naked thighs, facing the delicious flesh of her vagina, let her feel your warm breath moving closer and closer to your goal. When you reach that goal, lift your head a bit and open your lips wide, then close them softly over her furry mons, pressing that and moving your head from side to side until she begins to react; and when she does, let your hand take the place of your lips over that sensitive puff, so your lips can move on to better things.

Lower your lips so they are poised in front of her labia (the outer lips of her vagina), pucker them as if for a kiss, and begin moving your head from side to side, letting your lips brush her thigh, her labia, her outer thigh. Soon her clitoris will rise to receive its share of these brushing kisses, and her cries of delight will rise along with it.

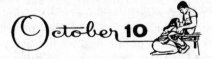

October 10

Even the best position for sexual intercourse is only as good as you make it, and tonight you are going to show her how a very good position can be made into one that is terrific.

And that means terrific for both of you!

When you are ready to make love, ask her to lie on her side and draw her knees up as far as she can, until they are touching her breasts, if possible. That is her part of the position, and here is yours.

Use your hands to spread her thighs and, slipping between them so that your body forms a right angle to hers, guide your hardened penis into her vagina. You will find it parted and ready.

And you will find this position—much like a standard rear-entry one—allows you to drive the full length of your hardened penis into hidden places it has never before touched.

She will surely be touched by the touching.

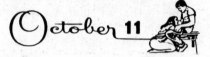

Here is an exercise in sensuality you should know and practice. It is designed to help you become the kind of lover you want to be, and, more important, the kind she wants you to be.

Stand with your hands on your hips and slowly begin to pump your hips back and forth. Do this for a moment and then try to move them in slow circles, squares, figure eights and any other patterns you can imagine. These are the motions of the expert lover, and if you think they are for women alone, you have another think coming.

Repeat these hip exercises often and you will find they soon come naturally when you are with her. You will also find that your chances to use them with her will become more frequent.

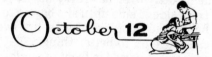

Do a little searching through her drawers (the ones where she keeps her clothing, that is!) and find the softest, most breast-hugging sweater she owns. Ask her to wear it for you, and ask her to wear it without a bra. Coax her into this by telling her you want to see the tempting sway of her beautiful breasts as she moves about, that you love being able to see the outline of her luscious nipples. This is the kind of talk she loves to hear, and you will soon have her agreement.

Then take her out into public and let her see you staring at those delightful spheres with greedy eyes. You will soon see the nipples begin to swell and harden, for you are exciting her in several ways. Your own obvious desire and admiration is the first.

More stimulation will be given by the soft wool against her naked breasts, for it is one of the most arousing materials a woman can feel against her nipples, and still more will come from knowing she is sexually arousing you in a public place; this caters to the mild exhibitionistic tendencies found in most women.

That last tendency, if you are really lucky, will come to the surface later, when she stands before you wearing only that sweater—no slacks or skirt, no panties . . . nothing!

October 13

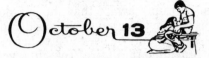

Role-playing is a major part of all our lives. There is no person who does not do it to one extent or another. We all tend to behave (or misbehave) in ways that we think will have a desired effect on those around us, though this is usually done without conscious thought. This role-playing can be a tremendous aid to those hoping to overcome their sexual inhibitions, so why not put it to use tonight? You will be glad you did.

Explain this playing of roles to her just as it was described above and then ask her to try this experiment with you. Let her select a character role for you to play that is totally foreign to your normal behavior (brute, little boy, rapist?) and you select a role, using the same criteria, for her (virgin, prostitute, nymphomaniac?). Now act out these roles while making love!

Both of you will discover that it is wonderfully easy to talk and behave in an uninhibited manner when the other person expects you to do so, and the mood of freedom created by this little pastime may be such that neither of you will ever again find it necessary to feel inhibited.

At least not with each other.

October 14

Tell her there is a peeping Tom outside the window!

Wait until you have finished making love and suddenly sit up to stare at the window. Put one finger to your lips, as if to silence her, slip on a robe and rush out of the room. Return after a few moments and tell her a man was watching as the two of you had sex, but he managed to escape.

Would you believe some women are excited by the thought of making love while being watched. It is true, and while she may not be among this group, she will still admire the bravery you displayed in chasing the intruder away.

In either case you are likely to find yourself repeating the act the nonexistent intruder supposedly watched.

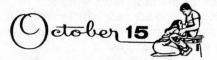

October 15

You are almost certainly aware that she is aroused by looking at erotic photographs or films, but have you considered the many ways in which this visual stimuli may be used to give her real sexual pleasure instead of merely providing the desire? Tonight try the way that is probably the best of them all—for you and for her.

Select a book containing a wide variety of erotic photographs and get her interested in them. Then, while her eyes are locked on the pages, begin stroking her body with your hands, lavishing slow kisses on her with your lips. Let the kisses wander across her breasts and stomach to the cleft of her vagina, and then lick her till you hear the book hit the floor. Her mind will be filled with, and her senses stimulated by, erotic imagery as the two of you make fantastic love.

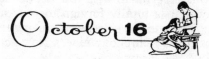

October 16

Put a little color in your lovemaking!

Stop by a drug counter, a bookstore dealing in erotica and sex aids, or check the vending machines found in men's rooms, and you will discover that prophylactics are now available in a wide array of colors including black, orange, red, blue, and yes, even stripes. Buy a pack of the wildest colored ones you can find, don one tonight, and walk into the bedroom wearing it.

Her reaction may include a little laughter, but no relationship was ever hurt by that, and any laughter will turn to sighs of delight as she takes you in her arms for a closer inspection of this novelty.

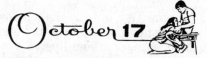

October 17

Ask her to dance with you in the privacy of your home, or, if you don't dance, ask her to teach you how.

No activity encourages a greater degree of physical contact than dancing, and no place is better suited for it than your own home, as you will discover when you dance holding her with hands that wander to more and more intimate areas of her body, and when she responds by pressing herself temptingly close to your rising erection.

But your discovery will be complete when this intimacy leads the two of you dreamily into the bedroom, for that is when you will really begin to see why dancing is so popular.

October 18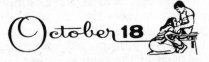

Try this technique of cunnilingus and tonight will be a night she will long remember, and you will be a man she will never forget.

Guide her lovingly onto her back, your hands and lips moving arousingly over her naked skin, and, turning, place yourself above her in the classic "69" position for simultaneous fellatio and cunnilingus—which is exactly what she may choose to make of it.

Lean far forward and place the tip of your stiffened tongue against the soft flesh at the very top of her vagina and move it slowly toward the rearmost part. When you have reached that, lift your head an inch or so, so your tongue makes no further contact, and move back to your delectable starting point. Repeat this over and over and she will soon be quivering in anticipation of the moment when your tongue moves across the front of her vagina, for that is when it moves delightfully over her swollen and throbbing clitoris.

October 19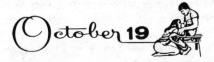

Tonight try this little prelude to sexual intercourse and be prepared to have a very loving woman in your arms.

When the last of her clothing has been removed and her naked body tempts you to complete what you have started, lower your mouth to her pubis, as if to perform cunnilingus, but avoid touching her vaginal flesh. Concentrate your attentions on the triangle of soft hair around it.

Run your tongue wetly over each curling tendril of this hair, lapping at it until her entire pubic area is wet. This hair itself is not susceptible to stimulation, of course, but the flesh beneath it is extremely so. When at last you take her in your arms and slide your hardened penis through the soft portals of her vagina, this wetness will prove delectable to her. And so will the tingling she feels in the places your tongue almost touched.

October 20

Take her into your lap tonight and show her how exciting the sitting position for intercourse can be when a very simple technique is used. She will be spending a lot more time on your lap.

When the two of you are naked and ready for love, sit down in an armchair, your legs only slightly parted, your penis hard and erect, and have her stand in front of the chair with her back to you. Put your hands on her hips to assist her as she sinks down onto your lap—and onto the hardened shaft of your penis.

When that is done, slip your arms around her, one hand going to her breasts, the other to the uppermost part of her vaginal lips, which will be distended and slightly parted by your intruding penis.

Now carefully, very carefully, use the tip of one finger to probe at these parted lips and locate the fleshy tip of her clitoris; it will be erected and easy to find. Let your finger caress it as lightly as possible and her purrs of delight will tell you you have found what you were searching for.

The clitoris is so sensitive to the touch that it is usually better stimulated by indirect pressure, but this is one of the few exceptions to that rule. It is an exception she will love.

You will find that she quite happily moves up and down in your lap, providing the motions of coitus and leaving your hands free to add to her pleasure, and you will find that she expresses that pleasure by reaching orgasm after. . . .

October 21

Sudden changes in body temperature, especially when they occur in the erogenous zones, can be tremendously arousing to either a man or a woman. So use a little cold to warm her up.

Catch her as she is leaving the shower and have an aerosol spray can in your hand. Teasingly spray her breasts, buttocks, pubic area, as many parts of her body as you can reach, and you will see her nipples harden as she reacts to the intense cold given off by these cans.

Use a can containing some food item, as these give off no toxins, and you are going to want to take her in your arms and use your lips to kiss away the chill.

October 22

Do you always perform cunnilingus in the bedroom? And always from the same position? And do you always perform it only briefly, as a prelude to sexual intercourse? Well, tonight, all these patterns are going to be broken—and she will love you for breaking them.

Take her into your arms while still in the living room and, after a few passionate kisses and caresses, slowly kneel and let your lips show her that you are eager to suck and lick her to orgasm.

Then remove her panties and proceed to do so.

But first guide her into an armchair and have her sit with her legs spread wide and resting over the arms. This position leaves her completely open for your sucking lips and licking tongue as you kneel before her, and it also gives a suggestion of brazen lewdness on her part—and that is something she may enjoy almost as much as your tongue.

Many women dislike—or at least gain less pleasure from—anal intercourse simply because most positions do not allow the man to kiss her lips or suck her breasts while in the midst of the act.

Tonight show her a position that does.

After applying lubricant to her anus, have her kneel so you may kneel behind her and insert your penis. When it is fully in her, slip your arms around her and roll to one side, taking her with you. Now lift yourself up on one elbow so you can lean over her, and use your hands to encourage her to twist her upper body toward you. This will allow you to lean down and kiss her lips and suck her rigid nipples to your heart's delight.

But it will really be to your sweetheart's delight.

Buy a bra and pair of panties, similar to those she normally wears but two sizes smaller, and secretly mix them in with her own underthings. Then sit back and wait. It may be a few days before she tries to put them on, and you may almost frighten her into a diet with this prank, but it will have results that are nice for you.

When she discovers they are too small, she can do nothing but take them off again. Offer her a little help.

Ask her to play this little game of word association. It is a good way to learn a little more about her thoughts and desires, and the words that pop out of your mouths may be a little surprising to both of you.

Say a word related to sex, or to a sexual part of the body, and have her respond instantly with the first word that pops into her mind, but tell her that it, too, must be sexual in nature. You then respond to that with the word it brings to mind, and so on. This can lead to some very interesting wordplay, and that can lead to some physical play of an entirely different nature.

October 26

Take her out to a lovers' lane—and go just as far as she and your own common sense will allow you to go.

If you recall the days when you first began to date, you will agree that there was a certain excitement in knowing that, at best, you might be able to fondle and suck the breast of the girl you were with, or even get a hand on her vagina, but that was as far as you could go under the circumstances. Women are doubly excited by this sense of pleasure desired but beyond reach.

But let her think you are "going to go all the way," as the kids put it. Do everything you can to arouse her and make her think you are willing to take the risk of copulating in the car, and stop just short of doing it.

Then get her home as fast as you can.

October 27

You know she is flattered and delighted when you pay special attention to her breasts, so tonight, after beginning your special attentions by taking those delightful mounds into your mouth and sucking and licking them till the nipples are erect and throbbing, why not turn that special attention around in a way that she will find even more thrilling?

Tell her how much you love the feel of her naked breasts touching your skin and let her know you would like to enjoy that same sensation over your entire body. Ask her to press those naked spheres against your chest, thighs, your groin—everywhere!

Coax her into this and she will greatly increase her arousal as she teases you with those firm nipples and soft orbs, and this arousal will multiply if you continue those special attentions as the two of you are making love.

October 28

Tonight show her what is perhaps the most effective oral technique of all. It is a technique that will create orgasm after orgasm in any woman capable of having one.

Use sensual kisses and arousing touches of your hands to guide her into a comfortable position on her back and take a prone position between her thighs, facing the delectable pink flesh of her vagina, then slip your hands, palms up, under her sleek naked buttocks. Let her feel your warm breath on her flesh for a moment or two before placing your mouth against her vaginal lips.

Use your tongue to part these delicious petals of flesh and dart it between them, licking her with quick, up-and-down strokes, until you feel her clitoris begin to swell. Now run the tip of your tongue up one side of her clitoral shaft. Do this several times, and then begin to lick the other side. Most women enjoy the touch of a tongue far more on one side of this shaft than the other, and her reactions will tell you which side is which.

And knowing that, you will have not the slightest difficulty in licking her to almost endless orgasm.

October 29

Ask her to bend over backward for sex—and show her after it can be worth the effort! This is a standing position many women enjoy.

Place an armchair in the center of the floor and have her stand, naked, with her buttocks against the back of it. Stand facing her and take her hands in yours, then have her lean far, far back, spreading her legs as she does. This will cause her pelvis to lift, her pubis to swing forward, and you will be able to enter her quite easily.

But her pleasure may be such that you will have a little more difficulty getting out. So who cares?

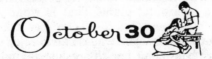

October 30

Beggars' Night!

This is the traditional night for trick-or-treat, so be wearing a mask or costume—any old kind will do—when you ring the doorbell. Tell her that if she refuses to give you a treat, you are going to soap all her windows, and make it clear that you are not going to settle for candy, apples, or popcorn balls. Tell her you would probably settle for the kind of treat she can give you in the bedroom, and she will probably agree.

After all, what woman wants her windows soaped?

October 31

Happy Halloween!

Make it an even happier one by making her the victum of this harmless little prank. Take her to a costume party, have a good friend trade costumes with you, and have this same friend make a mild but sexy pass at her. Let her discover the deception on her own. Just be sure of these things: Be sure the pass the guy makes is only a mild one; be sure he really is a friend; and be sure she knows it was all in good fun.

And be sure to make another pass when the two of you are alone.

November 1

Before actually entering into sexual intercourse tonight try this little technique that will make her almost desperate with the need to feel your hard penis slipping in and out of her vagina.

Have her lie on her back while you kneel between her legs, almost as if ready to start intercourse from this position, then reach back to grasp her legs behind the knees. Now lift her legs high, higher still, so they bend at the knees and those knees are as near as possible to her shoulders. This will, of course, cause her bottom to lift and it will place her vagina on a horizontal plane. That is what you were trying to accomplish.

Now swing your hips in closer, so the underside of the shaft of your hardened penis rests along the slit of her vagina, and begin slowly pumping your hips. This means your penis will be lightly brushing her outer vaginal lips and, as it rises in response, her clitoris. A few such strokes will have her reaching down to hold your erection tight against her aroused flesh, and when you lower her legs to enter her, that flesh will be hot, wet and responsive.

November 2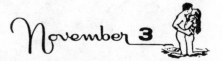

If you like the female-above positions for sexual intercourse, and she does not, it may be because you remain too passive when using them, as many men do. So tonight show her how dominant you can be while she is in the dominant position.

Lie on your back with your legs together and have her place one knee on each side of your body, her vagina directly over your erected penis. Place your hands on her thighs as her hot, wet flesh engulfs your erection. Let your hips roll and lift as she begins moving above you.

Now dig your heels into the bed, brace your shoulders, and curve your body into an upward arc, so she is literally suspended over your penis. Hold her there, moving your hips from side to side, and at the same time pull down, hard, on her thighs. Repeat this every few moments, always straining to drive your penis deeper, and she will soon be writhing in ecstasy.

And she will think you are anything but passive.

November 3

Tell her she has lint on the back of her skirt. This is something no well-dressed woman will tolerate, and she will gladly stand still as you run your hands over the firm swells of her buttocks in your efforts to brush away the imaginary lint. Find a little on her hips and thighs, even a little clinging to her hose, and get rid of that before having her turn so you can inspect the front of her clothing.

She will know you have been fibbing when you begin finding it on her breasts, but by that time she will be willing to forgive you.

She will also be ready to remove her clothes.

November 4

Tonight give her what many women believe is the ultimate in oral love. And give her a prolonged series of clitoral orgasms she will remember for as long as she lives.

Have her lie on her back while you lie on your stomach, facing her vagina and so close she can feel your breath. Cover the outer lips with tender kisses before probing between them with your stiffened tongue; then use that stiffened tongue to lick her until you feel her clitoris swelling and growing erect. That fully erect clitoris is the key to this technique, and it is what you have been trying to create with these preliminary efforts.

Catch the very tip of it between your lips and suck gently, drawing a bit of it into your mouth. Relax the suction. Draw it in once more. Release it. Do this over and over again, with increasing frequency, and she will be clawing at the back of your neck as her sweet, warm juices fill your mouth.

November 5

Does it excite you to imagine her dressed only in a black rubber bra so tight that her breasts swell upward to flow creamily over its cups and matching panties so tight they seem to cut deeply into the flesh of her buttocks and inner thighs? Well, you are not alone in this, for many men find female garments made of rubber the most exciting of all, and she may be more eager to wear them for you than you think; that is because most women are excited by anything that makes them more attractive to a partner in love.

So stop by a store and pick out a few erotic items you think would look especially sexy on her; you can find them at any store selling sex aids, at many bookstores handling erotica, and at places selling exotic female clothing.

Though she may not want to wear these every night, and may even seem a little hesitant at first, she will, if she is like most women, be excited by your sexy gesture—and that, really, is all that matters.

November 6

Remind her that on this date in 1869 Rutgers defeated Princeton by a score of 6 to 4 in the first college football game ever played, and use this as an excuse to challenge her to a game of touch football. On all plays following the kickoff, since there are no other players to serve as center and blockers, the defensive player will have to remain a few feet behind the line of scrimmage until the ball is put into play.

Now forget about the score and concentrate on doing all the touching you can . . . in the most intimate spots you can manage.

November 7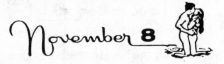

Making love while your shadows frolic on the walls around you can be a unique and erotic experience, as the entwining shadows add a great deal of visual stimuli to the sensations created in her body by your stroking hands, softly caressing lips, and thrusting penis. You can create these shadows by placing lamps on opposite sides of the bed, thus casting them on any wall she may face. It creates an illusion she will love, so why not create it tonight?

November 8

Begin this exercise in sensuality today, and be sure to practice it often. It will help you become a skillful and totally thrilling lover.

Form a circle with the thumb and first finger of your hand. Hold this circle in front of your mouth and extend your tongue through it, trying not to touch the edges of the circle. Now draw your tongue back into your mouth, again trying not to touch your fingers. Do this over and over, faster and faster, and as you find it becoming easier to do, let your thumb and finger form a smaller circle.

November 9

Tonight show her an oral technique that is slow, slow, slow—but all the more enjoyable to her because of this calculated slowness. And it is slow in the way it is applied; her orgasms will come in a quick series that will leave her shaken.

So let your lips be a little slow on her "trigger" tonight.

Kneeling between her naked thighs, in any position which allows you to cover with your lips the upper part of her vagina, use your mouth and tongue to stimulate her clitoris to erection. Part your lips and capture as much of this delectable flesh between them as you can, then draw your lips away, as if to tug slowly and gently on it, but allow it to slip slowly free. Suck it into your lips and again pull softly upon it, letting it slide away from your grasp.

Mix this with an occasional lap of your tongue, and she will soon be holding you in a grasp from which you will never want to escape!

November 10

How well do you understand the most potent erogenous zone of her body, her clitoris? If you know nothing else about her sexuality, you should know all there is to know about this center of her pleasure. You should understand that it resembles in many ways the male penis, that it grows erect and sensitive under stimulation, and though it does not ejaculate, as does the penis, its nerves are the ones controlling and responsible for her orgasms. You should know that her clitoris may be larger or smaller than that of another woman, that it may or may not be totally concealed by a "hood," and that the shaft of the clitoris may be the major source of her pleasure or it may be the very tip. Most of all you should realize that her clitoris is not exactly like that of any other woman; each female is an individual, and she will have her own individual reactions to clitoral stimulation of various types.

So you must learn—and tonight is the time—how she reacts to each and every type of clitoral stimulation, and you must learn which parts of her clitoris give pleasure when caressed and which parts you should avoid.

Learn these things by paying special attention to her reactions as you touch with your fingers and lick with your tongue the various parts of this moist pink flesh, and don't hesitate to learn even more by asking which spots give her the most pleasure.

That is the kind of information she will gladly give you.

November 11

On this date in 1918 World War One was brought to an end by the signing of an armistice. You would not want to let this day slip by without some sort of observance, so why not make it one both of you will enjoy?

Type up an official-looking document beginning, "I, (her name), hereby agree to make love with (your name) whenever and wherever he so desires." And anything else you wish.

Then ask her to sign your "Piece Agreement."

November 12

You are going to have to exercise a good bit of willpower tonight, but the luxurious sexual thrills you give her by doing so will make it worth the effort—and more!

As the two of you prepare to make love, insert your penis into her vagina *before* it reaches full erection (this may require a little help from her) and let her feel it growing larger and harder within her body. Her vagina must expand to accept your erected penis, and this slow expansion, while you kiss her lips and fondle her breasts, will add to her enjoyment of the hard, driving thrusts soon to follow.

November 13

Here is a very unusual sex position that she may enjoy, for it combines the pleasures of rear-entry intercourse with a kneeling position (on her part) that allows her to have some control over the depth of penetration. You can bet she will choose to make that penetration as deep as possible.

Lie on your back with your legs together and have her kneel with her vagina poised over your erection, her face toward your feet. Let her lower herself onto your shaft, settle into the motions of intercourse, and then, placing your hands on her hips, pull yourself into a sitting position. She can continue to lift herself over your penis, and you, with your hands stroking her nudity, can drive her into the realm of ecstasy.

November 14

Sexual intercoures can be at its delicious best when entry is made from the rear, and tonight's position and the technique you are going to combine with it will provide a thrilling experience she will long remember. And one you will not soon forget.

Have the wall or a heavy piece of furniture behind you, as you are going to lean far, far back during this act of love and will need something there for support. Have her kneel so you can enter her from the rear, and when this is done, reach down and around to fill your hands with the delightful spheres of her breasts. Now hold her tight as you straighten your body, bringing her with you, and even tighter as you lean far back, curving both your bodies into a bow. Your hard penis will be solidly in contact with her clitoris.

Hold it there, with your groin tight against her buttocks, your penis thrusting into her at an upward angle, and she will soon be a writhing bundle of beauty in your arms.

November 15

Does she have a sense of humor about sex? She should, because a touch of humor is good for any relationship, including a sexual one; and if she never laughs about sex, it may be because *you* have made no attempt to instill a little fun into your lovemaking.

Tonight is the night to bring that humor to life.

Use a red ribbon to tie a bow around your penis. Tie it tight enough so it will remain in place, but not tight enough to cause any problems. Then tell her you have a present for her. Few women can resist looking for a present that is obviously concealed, even when a search of your clothing tells her it must be hidden elsewhere, and she will look until she finds it.

Be sure she is quick to unwrap it.

November 16

The position you take when performing cunnilingus can be almost, but not quite, as important as the oral techniques you use. The position you are going to use tonight will add to her excitement because it gives her the distinct impression that you are ravenously hungry for the taste of her sweet, moist vagina.

And you are, aren't you? So show her.

When she lies naked and waiting for the touch of your tongue, kneel between her legs, your body erect and your knees close to her feet; then reach down and grasp one of her ankles in your hand, lifting it until your arm is fully extended above your head; at the same time slip your other hand under her buttocks, lifting them so her weight is thrown onto her back. Bend the elbow of this arm beneath her and you will find that the prop it forms makes it quite easy to hold her in this position while you lean down to lick her quivering loins. A tremendous position for cunnilingus!

November 17

If the way to a man's heart is through his stomach, as they say, the way to a woman's is to let someone else do the cooking for a change. So take her out for a nice dinner.

Pick a quiet, intimate restaurant, one that will allow you to really enjoy each other's company, and be sure it is one that serves her favorite food and serves it in a romantic atmosphere.

Just think of what she can do with the energy that might otherwise be wasted on doing the dishes.

November 18

Tonight, using a battery-powered massage device of the type designed to strap on the back of the hand (these cost very little are readily available, and they are a great sexual asset), show her the delights you can give her by combining oral skills with exotic anal stimulation. It is a combination few women will fail to appreciate.

Have her stand naked before you while you run the hand bearing the tingling device over her breasts, stomach, and buttocks, eventually dropping to your knees and caressing her thighs as your lips kiss their way toward the flesh and fluff of her pubis. Put the hand wearing the vibrator over her buttocks and urge her pelvis forward as you first begin to kiss and lick this center of feminiity.

At the same time let her feel your vibrating fingers squeezing and stroking the mounds of her buttocks, moving closer and closer to the cleft between them; and then let her feel one finger gently probing into this cleft. Press the tip of this finger against her anus and keep it there while you continue to lick her vagina; and then, when her body goes taut and begins to tremble with the approach of orgasm, push the finger deep into her anus and hold it there.

You will almost be able to feel the vibrations in the squirming, moistening vagina that presses against your face.

November 19

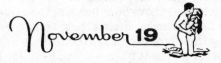

Every woman loves receiving a thoughtful card from the man in her life, especially when it is sent for no other reason than as a token of affection. That is why there is such a market for those cards which say, "Just thinking of you."

But why not be a little origianl and show her what you were thinking? Buy one of these cards, then use a Polaroid camera to take a picture of your hand gripping your erected penis, and paste this picture in the card.

Beneath the words "Just thinking of you," you might want to add, "as usual."

November 20

Cunnilingus is usually more exciting to her if she is able to look down the length of her naked body and watch your face moving between her upper thighs as your tongue darts hotly in and out of her vagina, but here is a technique that may be even more pleasurable precisely because she will never know where to expect the next arousing touch of your tongue.

That is because you are going to be behind her.

Have her lie on her stomach and spread her legs as far as she possibly can. You take a prone position between them and place both hands on the mounds of her buttocks. Ease your head in between her thighs and let your tongue begin to dance lightly over the flesh of her vagina—and into it—skipping from place to place. At the same time, press down on her buttocks, rotating them with your hands, and hear her sigh as she feels the pressure this creates on her mons. It is a method of cunnilingus many women believe to be at its very best.

November 21

Make an erotic tape recording. Address your words to her and describe in great detail the beauty of her body, the joy that body gives to you during the act of love, and the type of love you intend to give her later this evening. Be very explicit.

Leave the tape in the recorder, leave the recorder where she is certain to find it, and go about your business.

Just be ready to fulfill your promises after she hears that tape.

November 22

Take advantage of her while her hands are in the dishwater!

Simply walk up behind her while she is doing the dishes, catching her when she is up to her elbows in suds, and press your body tight against hers, your groin against her buttocks, your lips on the back of her neck, your hands on her hips . . . for the moment.

Grind your hips against her rear, letting her feel your erection growing against her buttocks while at the same time pressing her pubis against the front of the sink and let your hands begin to wander.

Let them cup and fondle her breasts, stroke her thighs, and slip under her skirt. She may protest at first, but you will notice that, if she is like most women, she will not use her hands to stop you. That may be because they are soapy—but it is probably because she wants you to continue.

November 23

Tonight show her how exciting a kiss can be!

The way you kiss greatly affects her response to your lovemaking, and this is a method of kissing that is extremely arousing to most females. And it may be even more arousing to you.

When you take her in your arms and kiss her, encourage her to thrust her tongue into your mouth by letting her feel yours dart between her lips. When she responds, as she will, close your teeth lightly over her tongue. Hold it just tight enough to let her feel the resistance as it withdraws, and capture it this way time after time. Use your hands to caress her breasts and buttocks as you do this and soon she will be eager to feel the thrusts of *your* tongue.

But she won't want to feel it thrusting into her mouth.

November 24

Show her that she is the girl of your dreams!

Pretend to fall asleep while she is still awake and let her hear you talking softly in your sleep. Make her believe that you are dreaming about sex, and make her believe you are dreaming about having sex with her. Let your words tell her you are enjoying it, and sigh her name each time you express your pleasure.

She will soon wake you up and you will be doing it instead of dreaming about it. What a dreamy way to seduce her!

November 25

Here is a sex position both of you will love. You will love it because, among other reasons, it allows you to see each glistening inch of your penis as it slides in and out of her body. She will love it because it provides maximum friction against her clitoris while allowing her to feel your penis sliding in and out of her vagina as fast or as slow as she wishes.

Lie on the floor, on your back, and have your feet about twelve inches from the base of an armchair. She then straddles your body, her face toward your feet and the armchair, and grasps the edges of the seat as she assumes a kneeling position and lowers herself onto your erected penis. Her hands on the edge of the chair will provide leverage that allows her to rock up and down with incredible speed, or to hold herself suspended at any point she chooses; and your hands on her buttocks will cause her to choose to continue until both of you are satisfied as never before.

November 26

Solve the puzzle of sex!

Paste the most beautiful, most explicit, erotic photograph you can find onto a sheet of cardboard. Let it dry and use a razor blade to cut it into small, irregular pieces, creating a jigsaw puzzle. Put the pieces into a box, shake them up, and ask her to help you work the puzzle. She will stare at you as if wondering what is on your mind.

But she will soon get the picture.

November 27

The classic position for simultaneous cunnilingus and fellatio, referred to in slang as the "69" position, usually has the man over his female partner, leaning down to lick her vagina while she lifts her head to kiss and suck his penis. This is simply because it is usually the male who initiates the oral action. Tonight try reversing the position and you may discover she is much more eager to participate in this delight-filled act.

As you lie beneath her with your head lifted between her parted thighs and your tongue moving hot and wet through her vagina, the sheer comfort of her position is going to make it far more enjoyable for her to lean down and cover you with her mouth.

So why not let her come out on top for a change?

November 28

Do you always strip away each and every bit of her clothing before making love to her? If you do, you may be denying her the pleasure many women receive by having intercourse while partially clothed and with the remaining bits of clothing in a state of disarray. It may be that this excitement is caused by a sense of eagerness on your part, of force, or of haste, or of tasting forbidden fruit, but in any case it is there and tonight you should see that she enjoys it.

During the foreplay, instead of stripping her naked, lift her sweater or blouse and tug the cups of her bra down, so her breasts are naked and forced upward by these cups; and instead of removing her panties as you lean down to kiss her vagina, simply tug the crotch to one side and hold it there as your tongue darts between the petals of flesh. Do the same when you make love and she will love you for doing it!

November 29

Her nipples are among the most potent of her erogenous zones, and there are countless ways you can caress, stroke, kiss, bite, suck or fondle them and add to her sexual pleasure; but none is more delightful to her than the technique you are going to use tonight.

When those delightful spheres are naked and cupped in your hands, when you are preparing to make love (or, better still, while you *are* making love!), suck the nipple into your mouth and capture it between your lips. Tug it gently a few times and then, with your lips still closed around it, begin flicking it rapidly up and down with the tip of your tongue. You will almost literally taste her delightful pleasure.

November 30

Sneak out to the fusebox and remove the main fuse. That means no radio, no television, no nothing to interfere with the making of love by candlelight. If you think that modern gimmicks such as TV do not tend to interfere with sexual activities, then you have another think coming. It is a fact that, nine months after the huge blackout on the East Coast a few years ago, maternity wards in the area were crowded as never before.

So why not create your own little blackout?

December 1

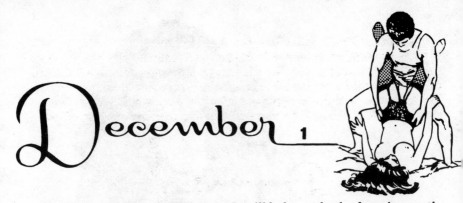

Try this exciting prelude to sex. It will help put both of you in exactly the right mood for the love that is soon to follow.

As you lie kissing her lips and stroking her breasts and buttocks, the full length of your body touching hers, place the shaft of your erected penis between her thighs, as high as possible, and let your hips begin to pump slowly. The feel of your erected penis, hot, hard, and moving, is the most exciting caress you can give her. You may feel her thighs tightening around it as you thrust it back and forth, but not for any great length of time.

Because soon she will want to feel it higher.

December 2

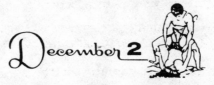

Time to start thinking about that Christmas shopping and preparing a list. The thing to remember when selecting her gifts is that she wants to receive presents that express your affection, that last, and that will remind her of you. And no gift will do this better than a gift you have made. Think about it.

Each person has a skill of some sort, no matter how limited, and the painting, poem, or piece of woodwork you have created is something she will cherish long after your other gifts are forgotten.

So give a little of yourself this Christmas.

December 3

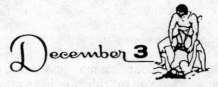

Here is an exercise in sensuality that will help you develop the control needed to give her the tender caresses of the tongue she really

162

wants to feel. Try it today and practice it regularly.

Place a small, soft piece of fruit such as a strawberry between your lips and hold it there. Now use the tip of your tongue to move it toward the left corner of your mouth, back to the center, and then to the right. Try to do this without dropping the fruit or breaking its skin. It is no easy task—but she will be more responsive because of your efforts.

December 4

Her mouth, as you probably know, can be a potent erogenous zone, though her arousal is probably caused to a large extent by psychological factors and to a lesser extent by physical ones. By knowing this and using it you can give her far greater pleasure when pressing your lips to hers.

Tonight, as you thrust your tongue deep into her mouth, remember that this is suggestive of the thrusting penis, of cunnilingus, or of fellatio; the flickering of your tongue may bring faintly into her mind images of that same tongue flickering across her nipples.

But the most arousing thing of all may be when she uses her mouth on various parts of your body, so tonight why not encourage her to do just that?

She may never again need encouragement.

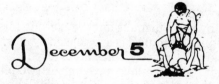

December 5

Take her for a piggyback ride—without asking!

Sneak up behind her while her mind is occupied, duck down and slip your head between her thighs, wrapping your arms around her legs, and lift her onto your shoulders as you stand. Then take off on a wild, bouncing, frolic throughout the entire house.

This is a playful show of masculinity most women will love, and as she rides with her thighs over your shoulders, her pubis against the back of your neck, all that bouncing may just create some sensations that will cause her to want you to "ride" *her* in an altogether different manner.

163

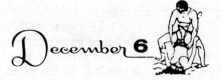

$\mathcal{D}$ecember 6

Cunnilingus supreme! That is how this technique is best described, and she will agree it is just that after tonight.

After removing her panties and bra to reveal the most tempting parts of her body, have her lie on her back while you sit close beside her on the bed, one hand stroking her breasts and the other slipping under her naked buttocks. Lift her buttocks with that hand and, leaning down, place your open mouth over the soft, hair-covered mound (the monds) above her vagina. Press down firmly with your mouth and move the fleshy rise in slow circles, while at the same time using one hand to fondle her breasts, the other to lift and knead her buttocks.

Continue to orally manipulate her mons for a few moments, then let her feel your tongue flickering across it again and again, each lick a little closer to her vaginal lips; then, finally, let her feel your tongue prying these lips apart.

You will find they separate quite easily.

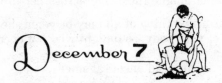

$\mathcal{D}$ecember 7

The male-above or "missionary" position for sexual intercourse may be varied in many ways to make it more exciting for the two of you, but here is a technique so simple it is overlooked by most couples. That may be because looking is exactly what is involved.

As you prepare to make love have one or two pillows placed so she may rest her head on them and so her head will be slightly lifted. This will allow—even encourage—her to look down the length of her naked body as the two of you are making love . . . and that is what you want her to do.

When you are above her and making love, try pausing for a moment and holding yourself at arm's length over her, so that only the tip of your penis is nestled in her vagina. Lower your eyes suggestively to look at the union of your bodies, and hers will surely follow. Pause in this manner several times during the act of love and you will find her staring, entranced, at the slick, warm shaft from which she is receiving such incredible pleasure.

December 8

Really get into cunnilingus tonight!

When her skimpy panties have been removed by your stroking, arousing hands, when she lies on her back with her thighs parted, her vagina hot and waiting, take a prone position between her legs and let your kisses lead the way to the delectable flesh of her loins.

With your face pressed tight to that pink and coral flesh, and your hand massaging the sensitive mound above it, dart a stiffened tongue into her vaginal well, licking and lapping her until she is wet and her clitoris is erected.

Now use your fingers to carefully, very carefully, spread wide the outer lips of her vagina; then, pressing your lips as tight as possible to her, release her, letting her labia fold around your own lips. When this is done, suck for a long moment at the soft flesh before you, then dart your tongue as deep as possible into her vagina. Use the tongue, then suck. Use the tongue then suck again.

That is really getting into cunnilingus!

December 9

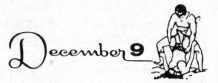

There is no better way to show her the pleasure that anal stimulation can provide than to let her see how truly exciting it is to you. Men also are subject to anal arousal (and it is not the mark of the homosexual, as many believe), in case you didn't know, and seeing your own reactions to this stimulation may help her to overcome any inhibitions she has about analism.

So let her see those reactions tonight!

As the two of you are making love, or as she fellates you (lucky man!), silently take her hand and guide it around to your buttocks, holding it there and shifting your body until she gets the idea and you feel her finger probing your anus. That is likely to be very soon.

Every experienced fellatrice knows that a finger in the anus of the male will greatly increase the pleasures she gives with her mouth, and, as her finger begins to move faster and faster through your anus, keeping pace with your lovemaking, the two of you will see why this is so. And she is likely to want to enjoy this herself.

For seeing is believing, as they say.

December 10

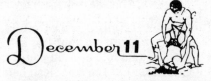

On this day in 1920 Woodrow Wilson received the Nobel Peace Prize. Commemorate this historic occasion by giving her an award of your own. (If Nobel can do it, why not you?)

Make up an official-looking scroll. Across the top have a heading that reads: *The* (your name) *Piece Prize,* and below that let it say it is being presented to her *for her outstanding achievements, above and beyond the call of duty, in the bedroom.*

She will try to be worthy of the honor.

December 11

'Tis the season to be jolly, so hang a sprig of mistletoe overhead, anywhere in the house, then wait until you see her standing beneath it. Then kiss her both when and *where* she least expects it.

Just throw your arms around her waist, lower your head to plant a prolonged kiss on the sloping cleft of her pubis (she will feel it through her clothes, you know), and point to the mistletoe when she asks what brought this on.

She may choose to stand beneath it for hours.

December 12

Tonight show her a version of the female-dominant position for sexual intercourse that will prove incredibly exciting for both of you. She may ask you to repeat this one often . . . starting tonight.

Lie on your back with your knees drawn up and your thighs parted. Have her sit straddling you, with her vagina over your erection and her buttocks actually resting on your upper thighs, which are raised by the bending of your knees. She can then, quite literally, slide down with delicious slowness to engulf the hardened shaft of your penis, and she can lean back against your thighs as your bodies pump and weave together.

December 13

Holding the hardened shaft of your penis in her hand is something she takes great pleasure in doing, you know, for it is the equivalent of your placing your hand on her warm vagina, giving much the same pleasure; and it is in this manner that most females first have contact with the male organ, so many subconscious factors come into play when her hand encircles your hardened flesh.

Use these facts to increase her enjoyment during love tonight.

When your two bodies are locked together, after your thrusting penis has brought her to eager life beside or beneath you, withdraw your penis almost fully and guide her hand down to it. Wait until her fingers close around it and begin driving your penis slowly back and forth through her fist. This means that, momentarily at least, her fist will limit the depth of your penetration, but when that moment passes, when her hands slips away from your hardened shaft, you will find her pelvis lifting to meet you with a passion you never knew existed in her.

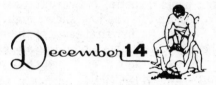

December 14

Try the female-dominant position for anal intercourse. It is the position you may come to prefer above all others, because it allows you to lie mouth-to-mouth, her breasts in your hands or touching your chest, while enjoying the mutual delights of having your hard penis gripped tightly by her anus.

What more could you want from a position?

Lie on your back with your legs together and have her straddle you, much as you would if having vaginal intercourse from this position but with her body a little higher along yours. Now, while you use one hand to hold your erected penis in position, have her reach back with both hands and hold her buttocks apart; she can then move her body slightly backward and let your penis slip into her rear.

After the initial entry has been accomplished, she can rock to and fro and control the pace of copulation, and the position can be varied in a number of ways; she can rise to a semierect position above you; she can press her body to yours and roll her hips; she can easily assume a kneeling position that will allow her to lower her weight on your penis and swallow it all.

Any way she chooses will be delightful!

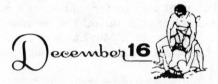

December 15

The sight of your hardened penis is exciting to her, as is the feel of it touching her naked skin, so why not combine these two sensory stimulants by letting her watch with fascinated eyes as your hardened shaft moves back and forth between the tempting spheres of her breasts? It is a combination she may find incredibly thrilling.

When she lies naked on her back, and after she has expressed her willingness, place one leg on each side of her body, straddling her, and take her softly yielding breasts in your hands as you move your hips closer to these delectable mounds. Now put your hands on the outer curves of her breasts, pressing them together, and shift your hips forward so your penis lies sandwiched in the soft valley between them. Slowly and teasingly move your hips back and forth.

The sight of your penis thrusting between those soft peaks can be a tempting sight to her, and it was just such a sight that led many a fellatrice to part her lips for her first taste of the male penis.

You know the beauty of her pubis is tempting and exciting to you and creates in you the desire to taste it, so is there any reason you should deny her this comparable opportunity?

December 16

Sex without affection is like bacon without eggs. And if she is not always enthusiastic about your lovemaking, it may be because you fail to display your affection before, during, and after the act.

Tonight put your love on display for her.

Let your lips cover her face and body with hot, arousing kisses before and during the act of love, while you repeatedly whisper words of devotion, and, more important, after the physical act is completed, hold her in your arms and let her feel how tender you can be.

Such expressions of love are usually more important to a woman than to a man—indeed, she probably sees them as the key ingredient in her relationship with you—and you will find she becomes more responsive to your sexual efforts if you fulfill your responsibilities in this area.

Make a conscious effort to do this tonight and every night in the future. It will make the future a happier one.

A happier one for both of you.

December 17

Tonight, when she lies naked and reaching for you with eager arms, be worthy of that eagerness by thrilling her with a type of cunnilingus that will have her quivering in orgasm long before you lift your face from her vagina and move up over her to fill her soft loins with the hard shaft of your penis. And when you do plunge your erected symbol of manhood into that velvety wetness, the two of you will know sex at its delightful best.

Parting her thighs with your hands, move between them and touch your lips to the warm flesh of her vagina, licking at her until she is wet with sexual lubricants, then press your face literally into her vagina and let your tongue curl downward, exploring the very rear of her vagina, even licking across it and attempting to touch the soft curves of her buttocks. Continue this until her wet pubis grinds excitedly against your face, then let your lips and tongue move upward to savor her clitoris and bring her to orgasm.

Again and again and again!

December 18

Show her a new angle in lovemaking!

Tonight, after using all your skills as a lover to bring her nerves alive and fill her body with eager anticipation, coax her into the same position—on her back, her legs slightly parted—that she would assume for intercourse in the common male-dominant position. Then give her incredible pleasure by using this variation on the old standby position.

Instead of settling your body between her parted thighs, as you probably do when otherwise using this position, straddle one of her legs with your own and use your hands to encourage her to twist her pelvis to the side, making it possible for you to enter her. With her leg extended between your own and her hips slightly turned, you will find it quite easy to enter her in this position—and the two of you will be glad you did.

By changing the angle of penetration in this manner, you cause your penis to make greater contact with vaginal areas that might otherwise receive only slight stimulation, and you will happily discover that it causes her vagina to feel tighter than ever before.

December 19

Your kisses can be the most important part of sexual foreplay, and these kisses are not doing all they are capable of doing if they are confined to her lips and face. Body kissing can arouse her as no other thing can do, so tonight, as the folks who publish the yellow pages of the telephone directory might say, let your kisses do the walking.

When she lies naked and ready for love, bend down over her and plant a lingering kiss on her breast, then skip suddenly from there to the other soft mound; move quickly to her thighs, then back up to her navel; back to her thighs, and from there, perhaps to her buttocks. The idea is to skip about and move quickly, not letting her know where to expect the next touch of your lips, but at the same time making it clear that your ultimate goal is the most sensitive area of all—her vagina.

She will tingle with anticipation as you near that goal.

December 20

Tonight show her a technique of cunnilingus that is so pleasing she will literally feel your tongue moving over her vaginal flesh long after you have finished making love and fallen asleep with your arms around her. She may even wake you up for an encore.

Sitting beside her on the bed (and the entire act, you should remember, will be more exciting to her if she is able to reach down and grasp your warm, hard penis), place one hand on the swell of her breast and the other on the fleshy, hair-covered mound at the very top of her pubis. Use this hand to press her mons and exert an upward pressure, as if tugging it toward her breasts. This pressure is not only pleasing to her but will cause her labia to part slightly, opening the way for what you are about to do.

Now lean down over her and thrust a stiffened tongue between those labia, reaching in as far as you possibly can; then let your tongue curl quickly upward, exactly as if you were trying to touch your nose with it; straighten the tongue, then curl it upward once more, and do this over and over, faster and faster.

She will curl up beside you, in pure ecstasy, when this night is over.

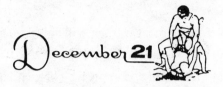

December 21

Ask her to take a chance on sex; she really can't lose!

After explaining what you want to do, and getting her agreement to give it a try, select an erotic novel and have her pick a page number. Open the book to that page and begin reading aloud. Stop when you come to the first sex scene, for whatever act is there described is the one the two of you have agreed to duplicate.

So duplicate it and then ask if she'd like to pick another number. Most women like a little mystery and suspense, so don't be surprised if she picks several.

December 22

The position you assume while performing cunnilingus can be of prime importance to her enjoyment of the act, and it can greatly influence the way she feels about taking your penis into her mouth and fellating you. Here is a position that openly invites her to do so, yet the suggestion is not as obvious as it might be if you assumed the famous "69" position while running your tongue in and out of her vagina.

Have her lie on her back with her thighs slightly parted, and you kneel near her shoulders, your face toward her feet. Slip one arm under her thighs and lift them, so her legs are drawn up toward her breasts, nearly touching them, and bent at the knees. Now urge her thighs wider apart and, still supporting her legs with your arm, lower your head to lick and suck her vagina. Not only is your hard penis conveniently close to her mouth, should she decide to taste it, but her position means she can clearly see your tongue darting over her pubis, and

171

that is a sight that is certain to encourage her to do so.

So give her that encouragement tonight.

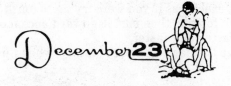

December 23

Sex should be fun, as most women will agree, so ask her to try this sexy little game with you. It may just become the favorite pastime of the two of you.

Ask her to leave the room and apply a bit of artificial flavoring to one small part of her body. It is then up to you to try to locate this, using your senses of taste and smell. Time yourself and then, after applying a bit of the same flavoring to your body, dare her to do better. It really makes little difference who wins, because you will have become interested in other matters long before the contest is over.

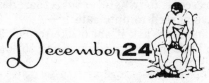

December 24

Christmas Eve.

This is the one season of the year that people, no matter what their religion, connect with love. It is the one season of the year when people (most of them, at least) are ready with a smile for even the stranger on the street. It is the season when you can create a happy, romantic mood simply by taking her out to mingle with the busy last-minute shoppers and letting the spirit of the season flow around you.

So take her for a hand-in-hand stroll along busy, tinseled streets, window-shopping and enjoying the hustle and bustle of those around you.

Then take her home to share tender moments before a flickering fire or a lighted tree, and be sure the two of you are tucked away in bed before midnight, when Santa is due.

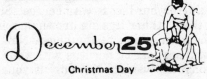

December 25
Christmas Day

Merry Christmas to you and to her!

No book should presume to tell you how to spend this day, but the authors and publishers of this book hope you are able to spend each and every minute of it together, with the warm glow of love surrounding you, and that the memories of this day are ones you will cherish for as long as you live.

December 26

Because the same nerves that cause her clitoris to be so highly sensitive to sexual stimuli extend into the area of her anus, the proper touches and caresses bestowed upon this latter region can cause her to derive far more pleasure from vaginal intercourse. If a sexual position allows you to bestow these caresses while your penis moves in and out of her tingling vagina, it is certainly a position worth trying.

So why not try this one tonight?

Sit in an armchair with your legs together and extended, and have her kneel facing you as she straddles your hips and lowers herself onto your erection. The beauty of this position is that it makes it perfectly natural for you to assist her movements by gripping the soft swells of her buttocks in your hands. And as she begins to move up and down on your penis, purring with pleasure as you lick and suck her breasts, what could be more natural—or more pleasing—than for your fingers to part those buttocks, stroking and flexing as they move closer and closer to her anus, not stopping until one is deep in her rear?

Nothing, that's what!

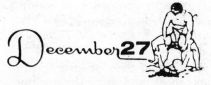

December 27

Use a swirling of your tongue to make her dizzy with excitement!

Tonight, after the touch of your hands and the soft caresses of your lips have urged her out of her clothing and she is beautifully naked before you, have her lie on her back with her legs spread wide. Take a prone position between those legs and cover her inner thighs with kisses as you move closer and closer to the pink and coral flesh of her vagina.

Now run your tongue teasingly over the outer lips until her hips begin to lift and weave, until her clitoris swells and is clearly visible at the upper center of her vagina; catch that softly between your lips and suck it into your mouth, as far as it will easily go. Still sucking gently, begin to move your tongue in a wide swirling motion inside your mouth, as if licking your inner cheeks. Roll your tongue about a dozen times in a clockwise direction, then reverse its direction. It will repeatedly caress her entire clitoral shaft, and each caress is going to be one she will love.

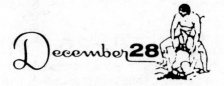

December 28

Tonight show her a variation of the standing position for sexual intercourse that is a favorite among knowing lovers, as it can be varied in several ways—without interruption.

Strip away her clothing and let her feel your hands and lips stroking and caressing her body as each item is removed, then lead her to a sofa or bed and have her stand facing it while you stand with your arms around her and your erected penis touching her rear.

Now have her lean forward and place her hands on the bed, supporting herself while you enter her; and then, after your penis is in, have her lift one knee and place it on the edge of the bed, extending her other leg to the rear. You will find that this shifting of the legs changes both the angle of penetration and the feeling of intercourse, and the joy of it all is that she can repeatedly switch the positions of her legs while you continue to drive your penis at her.

December 29

Sexual intercourse using the rear-entry position can be the kind of sex that she enjoys most, and using this technique will assure her of that enjoyment.

So why not use it tonight?

When she is naked and ready to make love, have her kneel on the bed, her buttocks slightly lifted, while you kneel behind her and prepare for the first thrust of your erected penis; but as you do so, place your knees so that one of her legs is between them.

Now insert your penis and let her feel it slipping in and out of her vagina, and as she begins to respond with rolling buttocks, grasp her thigh and draw it back between your legs, encouraging her to straighten and extend that leg.

Delightful! For both of you!

December 30

Tell her you have decided to become a Buddhist monk!

Make this announcement with a straight face; tell her you have been seriously considering it for quite some time; and add, as seriously and as sadly as you can manage, that this means you will have to abstain from all forms of sex.

Then take her in your arms, kiss her, and tell her you think you can wait until tomorrow before starting your abstinence.

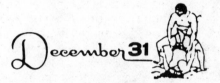

December 31

The last night of the year, so make it a good one.

Spend it alone, or take her to a party, whichever she prefers, but arrange to be together when the bells toll midnight. Take her in your arms, kiss her, and whisper softly as you tell her that you are going to spend the first hours of this young year making love to her in the most exciting ways—and that is plural, not singular—she has ever known.

Then kiss her again and tell her this is only

... The Beginning